DEVRY INSTITUTES

REVIEW GUIDE

FOR

ALGEBRA

PRENTICE HALL, Upper Saddle River, NJ 07458

Editor: *Sally Denlow*
Production Editor: *Dawn Blayer*
Supplement Editor: *April Thrower*
Special Projects Manager: *Barbara A. Murray*
Production Coordinator: *Alan Fischer*
Cover Manager: *Paul Gourhan*

Printed in the United States of America

10 9 8 7 6 5

ISBN 0-13-095287-7

Prentice-Hall International (UK) Limited, *London*
Prentice-Hall of Australia Pty. Limited, *Sydney*
Prentice-Hall Canada, Inc., *Toronto*
Prentice-Hall Hispanoamericana, S.A., *Mexico*
Prentice-Hall of India Private Limited, *New Delhi*
Prentice-Hall of Japan, Inc., *Tokyo*
Prentice-Hall Asia Pte. Ltd., *Singapore*
Editora Prentice-Hall do Brasil, Ltda., *Rio de Janeiro*

CONTENTS

CHAPTER 1   INTRODUCTION TO ALGEBRA

1.1 Adding Signed Numbers

Compare the quantities in each of the following.

> 4° below zero and 4° above zero
> a 9-yard loss and a 9-yard gain
> a withdrawal of $5 and a deposit of $5

Situations such as these require numbers other than the whole numbers 0, 1, 2, 3, ...
To distinguish these quantities, we use numbers with the signs + and −, such as +4 and −9.

A number line illustrates **signed numbers**. The arrows show that the line can be drawn indefinitely to the left and right.

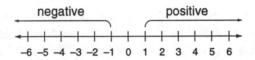

The number line shown above indicates that **integers** continue without end in both directions.

Since zero is neither **positive** nor **negative**, it is the only integer with no sign. Any other number recorded without a sign is assumed positive. For example, 5 = +5.

We say that 4 is less than 5. Notice that −5 is less than −4.

In the following examples, number line drawings illustrate addition of signed numbers.

Example 1 Find the sum of 4 and 2.

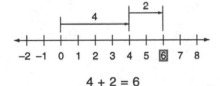

$$4 + 2 = 6$$

Example 2 Find the sum of −3 and −6.

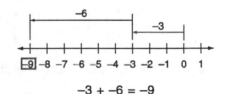

$$-3 + -6 = -9$$

Example 3 Find the sum of −4 and 7.

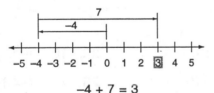

$$-4 + 7 = 3$$

Example 4 Find the sum of 3 and −5.

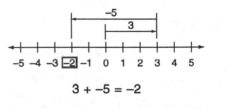

$$3 + -5 = -2$$

On the number line you can see that −6 and 6 are each 6 units from 0. We say that the **absolute value** of −6 is 6. The absolute value of 6 is also 6. The symbol for absolute value is a vertical bar on each side of the numeral.

$$|-6| = 6 \qquad |6| = 6$$

1

The absolute value of a number is the number of units it is from 0 on the number line. Absolute value can be used to find the sums of signed numbers.

Notice that the numbers being added in each of the following cases have the same sign as their sum.

$$4 + 2 = 6 \qquad\qquad -3 + (-6) = -9$$

These examples and others like them suggest the following rule.

> **To add numbers with the same sign, add their absolute values. The sum has the sign of the addends.**

Consider addends with different signs.

$$-4 + 7 = 3 \qquad\qquad 3 + (-5) = -2$$

Notice the difference between 7 and 4 is 3. Which addend has the greater absolute value? The sum has the same sign.

Notice the difference between 3 and 5 is 2. Which addend has the greater absolute value? The sum has the same sign.

These and other similar examples suggest the following rule.

> **To add numbers with different signs, find the difference of their absolute values. The sum has the same sign as the addend with the greater absolute value.**

If more than two signed numbers are to be added, start at the left and find the sum the first two numbers. Then add that sum to the next number and so on until all the numbers are added.

Write the absolute value of each number.

1. $+4$
2. $+3$
3. -19
4. -55
5. 82
6. -10
7. 10
8. 105
9. 0
10. -429

Name the sign of the sum in each exercise.

11. $-7 + (-7)$
12. $+2 + (+3)$
13. $9 + 2$
14. $-4 + 8$
15. $-20 + (-5)$
16. $-9 + 1$
17. $9 + (-19)$
18. $-1 + 10$

Find each sum.

19. $5 + 4$
20. $-6 + (-9)$
21. $-9 + 4$
22. $10 + (-12)$
23. $-4 + (-8)$
24. $-2 + 5$
25. $-8 + 8$
26. $74 + (-43)$
27. $33 + 25 + (-7)$
28. $15 + -9 + 4 + (-17)$
29. $3 + 40 + (-31) + (-2) + 3$

30. In four plays the Vikings gained 2 yards, lost 6 yards, gained 12 yards, and finally gained 3 yards. What was the net number of yards gained or lost?

31. Last month Tyler Thompson opened a checking account with a $300 deposit. He then wrote checks for $11, $7.95, $4.95, $175, and $15. Finally he deposited $50. The bank set Tyler a statement saying that the banking service charge was $3 for the month. What is the balance in Tyler's checking account?

1.2 Subtracting Signed Numbers

Subtraction is the inverse of addition. Compare subtraction with addition in the following. Numbers such as 3 an –3 are called **opposites**.

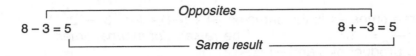

$$8 - 3 = 5 \qquad\qquad 8 + {-3} = 5$$

From these examples and others like them, we can conclude the following rule.

> **To subtract a signed number, add its opposite.**
> **If a and b are signed numbers, $a - b = a + {-b}$.**

Example 1 One night last winter the temperature fell from 14° above zero to 5° below zero. Find the difference in temperature.

The temperature fell from 14° to –5°. The difference was –5° – 14°.
Use the rule for subtracting signed numbers.
$$-5 - 14 = -5 + (-14) \qquad \textit{14 and } -14 \textit{ are opposites.}$$
$$= -19$$

The difference in temperature was –19°. That is, it was 19° colder.

Example 2 Find the difference in each of the following.

$$\textbf{a.}\quad 11 - 7 = 11 + (-7) \qquad\qquad \textbf{b.}\quad 4 - 9 = 4 + (-9)$$
$$= 4 \qquad\qquad\qquad\qquad\qquad = -5$$

$$\textbf{o.}\quad -8 - 8 = -8 + (-8) \qquad\qquad \textbf{d.}\quad -3 - (-14) = -3 + 14$$
$$= -16 \qquad\qquad\qquad\qquad\qquad = 11$$

Name the opposite of each of the following.

1. 2	**2.** 9	**3.** –1	**4.** 5
5. –4	**6.** 39	**7.** –1000	**8.** 109

Find the difference in each of the following exercises.

9. 39 – 23	**10.** –7 – 9	**11.** 11 – (–5)	**12.** –5 – (–8)
13. 2 – (–15)	**14.** 6 – (–1)	**15.** –2 – 2	**16.** –4 – (–19)
17. –8 – (–12)	**18.** 28 – 58	**19.** –1 – (–10)	**20.** –47 – 77

Answer each of the following.

21. Subtract –2 from the sum of 51 and –19.

22. Subtract the sum of 24 and –8 from –35.

23. On Friday the temperature was 3° below zero and on Saturday it was 8° below zero. Find the difference in temperature.

24. On Monday the temperature was 5° below zero. On Tuesday the temperature rose to 17° above zero. Find the difference in temperature on the two days.

1.3 Multiplying and Dividing Signed Numbers

Many multiplication problems may be thought of as repeated additions.

Example 1 Find the product of 3 and –4.

Three times –4 is the same as –4 + (–4) + (–4) or –12.
$3 \cdot (-4) = -12$ The *raised dot means "times."*
The product of 3 and –4 is –12.

The order in a multiplication problem does not affect the product. Therefore, $-4 \cdot 3 = -12$.

After checking many problems like these, we conclude the following rule.

> **The product of two numbers with different signs is negative.**

You know that $2 \cdot 3 = 6$. The product of two positive numbers is positive. Look at the patterns in the following problems. Start at the top problem and go down the column.

The first number in each problem is 1 less than the one preceding it.

$$3 \cdot (-3) = -9$$
$$2 \cdot (-3) = -6$$
$$1 \cdot (-3) = -3$$
$$0 \cdot (-3) = 0$$
$$-1 \cdot (-3) = ?$$
$$-2 \cdot (-3) = ?$$

The product in each problem is 3 greater than the one preceding it.

Since these patterns continue, $-1 \cdot (-3) = 3$ and $-2 \cdot (-3) = 6$. From these and other problems like them, we can conclude the following.

> **The product of two numbers with like signs is positive.**

Division is the inverse of multiplication. Consider the following problems.

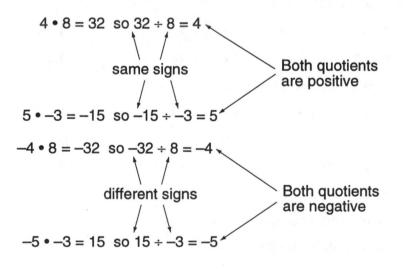

These problems and others like them show you that the rule for dividing signed numbers is as follows.

> **The quotient of two numbers with like signs is positive.**
> **The quotient of two numbers with different signs is negative.**

Example 1 Simplify $\dfrac{-9 \cdot -5 \div (-3)}{-6 \cdot 4}$.

Do the indicated operations from left to right in the numerator. Then, work with the denominator in the same way. Finally, reduce the fraction.
Note that if there is an odd number of negative factors, the answer is negative. If there is an even number of negative factors, the answer is positive.

$$\frac{-9 \cdot (-5) \div (-3)}{-6 \cdot 4} = \frac{45 \div (-3)}{-6 \cdot 4}$$
$$= \frac{-15}{-6 \cdot 4}$$
$$= \frac{-15}{-24}$$
$$= \frac{5}{8}$$

Name the sign of the product in each of the following.

1. $-3 \cdot 4$ **2.** $7 \cdot 6$ **3.** $-8 \cdot (-2)$ **4.** $3 \cdot (-1)$

5. $-2 \cdot 17$ **6.** $-4 \cdot (-10)$ **7.** $5 \cdot (-30)$ **8.** $-9 \cdot (-8)$

Name the sign of each quotient.

9. $4 \div 2$ **10.** $18 \div 9$ **11.** $30 \div (-5)$ **12.** $64 \div (-8)$

13. $-21 \div 7$ **14.** $-169 \div 13$ **15.** $-24 \div (-2)$ **16.** $-80 \div (-5)$

17. $\dfrac{-12}{4}$ **18.** $\dfrac{49}{-7}$ **19.** $\dfrac{-42}{-6}$ **20.** $\dfrac{55 \div 11}{-99 \div 11}$

Find the product or quotient in each exercise.

21. $6 \cdot 7$ **22.** $3 \cdot (-5)$ **23.** $-9 \cdot (-3)$ **24.** $3 \cdot (-2)$

25. $2 \cdot (-5)$ **26.** $-1 \cdot (-19)$ **27.** $44 \cdot (-2)$ **28.** $-7 \cdot (-11)$

29. $84 \div (-4)$ **30.** $-72 \div 8$ **31.** $56 \div (-2)$ **32.** $-64 \div 8$

33. $-69 \div 3$ **34.** $-144 \div (-9)$ **35.** $4 \cdot 2 \cdot 8$ **36.** $-8 \cdot 5 \cdot 4$

37. $3 \cdot (-3) \cdot 3$ **38.** $-5 \cdot (-1) \cdot 4$ **39.** $-3 \cdot (-2) \cdot (-2)$ **40.** $(-9) \cdot 4 \cdot (-2)$

41. Simplify $\dfrac{24 \div -4}{63 \div 9}$. **42.** Simplify $\dfrac{-18 \div 9 \cdot 3}{-6}$.

43. Simplify $\dfrac{-6 \cdot 8 \div (-12)}{-21 \div 3}$. **44.** Simplify $\dfrac{-8 \cdot 4 \cdot (-3) \div 32}{-1 \cdot (-5)}$.

5

1.4 Evaluating Algebraic Expressions

In 10^3, the 3 is the exponent and the 10 is the base. The following shows how exponents are used.

$$10 = 10^1 \quad \text{read} \quad \textit{ten to the first power}$$
$$10 \cdot 10 = 10^2 \quad \text{read} \quad \textit{ten to the second power or ten squared}$$
$$10 \cdot 10 \cdot 10 = 10^3 \quad \text{read} \quad \textit{ten to the third power or ten cubed}$$
$$10 \cdot 10 \cdot 10 \cdot 10 = 10^4 \quad \text{read} \quad \textit{ten to the fourth power}$$

An exponent tells how many times the base is multiplied. A **power** is a number written with an exponent.

The table below gives verbal expressions translated into algebraic expressions. Any letter, called a **variable**, may represent an unknown number.

Verbal Expression	Algebraic Expression
the sum of a number and 3	$x + 3$
50 decreased by a number	$50 - k$
40 times a number	$40a$
a number divided by 5	$\dfrac{w}{5}$

When variables are used in a product, such as $40a$, the multiplication symbol is usually omitted. The numbers multiplied in a product are called **factors**. A numerical factor is a **coefficient**. In $40a$, 40 and a are factors with 40 the coefficient. In xy, the coefficient is 1 because $1 \cdot xy = xy$.

You can find the values of expressions if you substitute specific values for the variables in the expressions. Then, do the indicated operations.

Example 1   Suppose $a = -3$ and $x = 2$. Evaluate $a - x$, $4a$ and $6a^3$.

$$a - x = -3 - 2 \quad \textit{Substitute } -3 \textit{ for a and 2 for x.}$$
$$= -5$$

$$4a = 4(-3) \quad \textit{A number before an expression in parentheses}$$
$$= -12 \quad \textit{is multiplied times the expression.}$$

$$6a^3 = 6(-3)^3$$
$$= 6(-3)(-3)(-3) \quad \textit{Notice that the base, which is negative,}$$
$$= 6(-27) \quad \textit{is a factor an odd number of times. Thus,}$$
$$= -162 \quad \textit{the product is negative.}$$

State a mathematical expression for each of the following.

1. the sum of w and 6

2. m decreased by 9

Write each of the following using exponents.

3. $2 \cdot 2 \cdot b \cdot b$

4. $4 \cdot 4 \cdot n \cdot n$

5. $7 \cdot 7 \cdot 7 \cdot m \cdot m \cdot n \cdot n$

6. $3 \cdot 3 \cdot 3 \cdot 3 \cdot t \cdot t \cdot t \cdot t \cdot t \cdot t \cdot t \cdot s \cdot s \cdot s$

Evaluate each of the following.

7. $m - n$ if $m = 75$ and $n = 31$

8. $d + f + h$ if $d = 7$, $f = 3$, and $h = 19$

9. ab^2 if $a = 6$ and $b = 8$

10. $3n^2 p^4$ if $n = 3$ and $p = 4$

11. $5xy^3$ if $x = -8$ and $y = -3$

12. $-10r^2 s^5$ if $r = -4$ and $s = -1$

6

1.5 Order of Operations

For an expression such as $3 - 4 \cdot 6$, the value would depend on the order in which the operations are done.

Subtract first.

$3 - 4 \cdot 6 = -1 \cdot 6$

$\qquad = -6$

Multiply first.

$3 - 4 \cdot 6 = 3 - 24$

$\qquad = -21$

└──────── *Different answers* ────────┘

So that the same problem will not have different answers, mathematicians have agreed to follow a definite order of operations.

1. Evaluate all powers first.
2. Then, do all multiplications and divisions from left to right.
3. Then, do all additions and subtractions from left to right.

With this agreement about the order of operations, what is the value of $3 - 4 \cdot 6$? You were right if you said -21.

You can indicate a change in the order of operations by using parentheses or other grouping symbols. Start with innermost set of grouping symbols. The horizontal bar in a fraction serves as a grouping symbol.

Example 1   Evaluate $5 + 2\left[8 + (4-2)^2\right]$.

$5 + 2\left[8 + (4-2)^2\right] = 5 + 2\left[8 + (2)^2\right]$

$\qquad = 5 + 2[8 + 4]$

$\qquad = 5 + 2[12]$

$\qquad = 5 + 24 \text{ or } 29$

Example 2   Evaluate $\dfrac{7-3}{2^4}(8)$.

$\dfrac{7-3}{2^4}(8) = \dfrac{4}{16}(8)$

$\qquad = \dfrac{1}{4}(8)$

$\qquad = 2$

In each of the following, name the operations in the order in which they are done. Do not evaluate the expression.

1. $1 \cdot 7 + 6$

2. $8 - 2 \cdot 7$

3. $3 \cdot 4 \div 2 - 9$

4. $3 \cdot 8 + 18 \div 3$

5. $(2-6) \div 4$

6. $7(1+2)^2$

7. $\dfrac{5+5}{2}$

8. $11 + \dfrac{3(7-5)}{6}$

Evaluate each of the following.

9. $10 - 2 \cdot 4$

10. $10 - 4 \cdot 2$

11. $3 \cdot 4 - 6 + 3$

12. $6(42 \div 7)$

13. $32 \div (4-2)$

14. $3 \cdot 9 - 9 \cdot 4 \div 4$

15. $18 \div 3 + 6 - 1$

16. $144 \div [(6+2) - 2]$

17. $7[2 + 2(2)]$

18. $200 \div [5(2+3)]$

19. $36 \div 6 + 2 - 3$

20. $81 \div [5 + (9-5)]$

21. $3(a+b)$ if $a = 2$ and $b = 0$

22. $39 - 3c^2$ if $c = 2$

23. $6m - (3n+1)$ if $m = 3$ and $n = 4$

24. $m^2 - (k^3 - m)$ if $k = 3$ and $m = 5$

25. $\dfrac{4(2b+a)}{c-1}$ if $a = 3$, $b = 2$, and $c = 3$

26. $\dfrac{r^2 + s}{n}$ if $r = 5$, $s = 2$, and $n = 9$

27. $\dfrac{a^2 + b^3}{c^2}$ if $a = 3$, $b = 2$, and $c = 5$

28. $\dfrac{a^3 + b}{c^2}$ if $a = 3$, $b = 1$, and $c = 2$

CHAPTER ONE SOLUTIONS and ANSWERS

Section 1.1

1. 4
2. 3
3. 19
4. 55
5. 82
6. 10
7. 10
8. 105
9. 0
10. 429
11. −
12. +
13. +
14. +
15. −
16. −
17. −
18. +
19. 9
20. −15
21. −5
22. −2
23. −12
24. 3
25. 0
26. 31
27. 51
28. −7
29. 13

30. The yards gained are positive and the yards lost are negative. $2 + -6 + 12 + 3 = 11$. The Vikings gained 11 yards.

31. Tyler's deposits are positive numbers. The amounts of checks and service charges are negative numbers.
$300 + -11 + -7.95 + -4.95 + -175 + -15 + 50 + -3 = 133.10$. Tyler's balance is \$133.10.

Section 1.2

1. −2
2. −9
3. 1
4. −5
5. 4
6. −39
7. 1000
8. −109
9. 16
10. −16
11. 16
12. 3
13. 17
14. 7
15. −4
16. 15
17. 4
18. −30
19. 9
20. −124
21. 34
22. −51
23. −5°; 5° lower

24. +22°; 22° higher

Section 1.3

1. −
2. +
3. +
4. −
5. −
6. +
7. −
8. +
9. +
10. +
11. −
12. −
13. −
14. −
15. +
16. +
17. −
18. −
19. +
20. −
21. 42
22. −15
23. 27
24. −6
25. −10
26. 19
27. −88
28. 77
29. −21
30. −9
31. −28
32. −8
33. −23
34. 16
35. 64
36. −160
37. −27
38. 20
39. −12
40. 72

41. $\dfrac{-6}{7}$

42. $\dfrac{-2 \cdot 3}{-6} = 1$

43. $\dfrac{-48 \div -12}{-7} = -\dfrac{4}{7}$

44. $\dfrac{-32 \cdot -3 + 24}{5} = \dfrac{96 + 32}{5} = \dfrac{3}{5}$

Section 1.4

1. $w + 6$
2. $m - 9$
3. $2^2 b^2$
4. $4^2 n^2$
5. $7^3 m^2 n^2$
6. $3^4 t^7 s^3$
7. $75 - 31 = 44$
8. $7 + 3 + 19 = 29$

9. $6 \cdot 8^2 = 6 \cdot 64 = 384$

10. $3 \cdot 3^2 \cdot 4^4 = 3 \cdot 9 \cdot 256 = 6912$

11. $5(-8) \cdot (-3)^3 = -40 \cdot -27$
$\quad = 1080$

12. $-10(-4)^2 \cdot (-1)^5 = -10 \cdot 16 \cdot -1$
$\quad = 160$

Section 1.5

1. Multiply, add
2. Multiply, subtract
3. Multiply, divide, subtract
4. Multiply, divide, add
5. Subtract, divide
6. Add, square, multiply
7. Add, divide
8. Subtract, multiply, divide, add

9. $10 - 2 \cdot 4 = 10 - 8$
$\quad = 2$

10. $10 - 4 \cdot 2 = 10 - 8$
$\quad = 2$

11. $3 \cdot 4 - 6 + 3 = 12 - 6 + 3$
$\quad = 6 + 3$
$\quad = 9$

12. $6(42 \div 7) = 6(6)$
$\quad = 36$

13. $32 + (4 - 2) = 32 + (2)$
$\quad = 16$

14. $3 \cdot 9 - 9 \cdot 4 + 4 = 27 - 36 + 4$
$\quad = 27 - 9$
$\quad = 17$

15. $18 \div 3 + 6 - 1 = 6 + 6 - 1$
$\quad = 12 - 1$
$\quad = 11$

16. $144 \div [(6 + 2) - 2] = 144 \div [8 - 2]$
$\quad = 144 \div 6$
$\quad = 24$

17. $7[2 + 2(2)] = 7[2 + 4]$
$\quad = 7(6)$
$\quad = 42$

18.
$$200 \div [(2+3)] = 200 \div [5(5)]$$
$$= 200 \div 25$$
$$= 8$$

19.
$$36 \div 6 + 2 - 3 = 6 + 2 - 3$$
$$= 8 - 3$$
$$= 5$$

20.
$$81 \div [5 + (9-5)] = 81 \div [5+4]$$
$$= 81 \div 9$$
$$= 9$$

21.
$$3(a+b) = 3(2+0)$$
$$= 3(2)$$
$$= 6$$

22.
$$39 - 3c^2 = 39 - 3(2)^2$$
$$= 39 - 3(4)$$
$$= 39 - 12$$
$$= 27$$

23.
$$6m - (3n+1) = 6 \cdot 3 - (3 \cdot 4 + 1)$$
$$= 18 - (12+1)$$
$$= 18 - 13$$
$$= 5$$

24. 3

25. 14

26. 3

27. $\frac{17}{25}$

28. 7

CHAPTER 2   EQUATIONS

2.1 Solving Equations

An **equation** is a mathematical sentence that says that two quantities are equal. The following equation says "Some number decreased by seven is nine."

$$x - 7 = 9$$

An equation that contains a variable is an **open sentence**. Without knowing what number the variable represents, you cannot say whether the sentence is true or false. You **solve** an equation by finding the number that will make the equation a true sentence when the number is substituted for the variable.

To understand how to solve $x - 7 = 9$, think of the equation as a scale in balance.

If the same number is added to each side of the equation, the new sentence also is in balance. Thus, this sentence also is an equation.

$$\begin{aligned} x - 7 &= 9 \\ x - 7 + 7 &= 9 + 7 \\ x + 0 &= 16 \\ x &= 16 \end{aligned}$$ *Add 7 to each side of the equation.*
        $-7 + 7 = 0$

In the last line above, just x is left on one side of the equation. This equation gives the solution for the original equation.

Check 16 by substituting it for x in $x - 7 = 9$. Because $16 - 7 = 9$, 16 truly is the solution.

To undo the subtraction of 7 in the original equation add 7. Recall that addition is the inverse of subtraction. To solve an equation involving division, you can use multiplication, the inverse operation. Consider the following example.

Example 1   Solve $\frac{x}{3} = -2$.

$\frac{x}{3} = -2$ *This equation says, " A number divided by 3 equals − 2."*

$\frac{x}{3} \cdot 3 = -2 \cdot 3$ *On each side, multiply by 3.*

$\frac{x \cdot 3}{3} = -6$ *x divided by 3 times 3 means the same as x times 3 divided by 3.*

$x \cdot 1 = -6$ $\frac{3}{3} = 1$

$x = -6$

Check. $\frac{-6}{3} \stackrel{?}{=} -2$

        $-2 = -2$ The solution is − 6.

10

These and other examples demonstrate that you can use the following rule to solve equations.

> **To solve an equation having one operation, do the inverse of that operation on each side of the equation.**

Example 2 Solve $7 = x + 4$.

$$7 = x + 4$$ *The inverse of the addition of 4 is the subtraction of 4.*
$$7 - 4 = x + 4 - 4$$ *Subtract 4 from each side. Then, $4 - 4 = 0$.*
$$3 = x$$

Check.
$$7 \overset{?}{=} 3 + 4$$
$$7 = 7$$ *The solution is 3.*

Example 3 Solve $5y = 10$.

$$5y = 10$$ *Dividing by 5 is the inverse of multiplying by 5.*
$$\frac{5y}{5} = \frac{10}{5}$$ *Divide each side by 5.*
$$y = 2$$

Check.
$$5 \cdot 2 \overset{?}{=} 10$$
$$10 = 10$$ *The solution is 2.*

State the operation you must do on each side of each equation to solve it. Also, state the number you would use.

1. $x - 22 = 14$

2. $y - 7 = -6$

3. $t + 5 = 10$

4. $6x = 24$

5. $-9t = 18$

6. $p - (-15) = 28$

7. $\frac{x}{3} = 2$

8. $\frac{k}{-7} = 7$

9. $-61 = k - 2$

10. $m + (-1) = -19$

11. $-36 = -3c$

12. $\frac{1}{2} = \frac{x}{5}$

Solve each of the following equations.

13. $d - 7 - 12$

14. $c - 3 - 21$

15. $n + 6 - 25$

16. $x + 17 = 47$

17. $b - (-7) = -1$

18. $m - (-2) = -5$

19. $b + (-2) = 38$

20. $\frac{k}{7} = 11$

21. $\frac{n}{5} = 20$

22. $w + (-15) = -15$

23. $5x = 30$

24. $7x = 98$

25. $\frac{u}{-3} = 19$

26. $\frac{t}{-2} = -45$

27. $-8t = 88$

28. $-3y = -54$

29. $m + 6 = 36$

30. $r + 5 = 21$

31. $\frac{x}{8} = 15$

32. $n - 12 = 14$

33. $\frac{c}{2} = -5$

34. $\frac{t}{-3} = 16$

35. $\frac{n}{7} = 19$

36. $6t = -66$

37. $n + (-4) = 15$

38. $-6x = 102$

39. $5w = 85$

40. $y - 0.25 = 4.75$

41. $3r = \frac{1}{3}$

42. $-6 + j = 38$

43. $\frac{x}{10} = \frac{2}{5}$

44. $m + 3\frac{1}{2} = 5\frac{3}{4}$

45. $1.5x = 9.9$

11

2.2 Equations with Solutions Involving Several Operations

An equation often involves more than one operation. Recall the order of operations used to evaluate a mathematical expression. To solve an equation with more than one operation, undo the operations in reverse order by using inverse operations. Study the following examples.

Example 1 Solve $4a + 7 = 31$.

$$4a + 7 = 31$$
$$4a + 7 - 7 = 31 - 7 \quad \textit{Subtract 7 from each side of the equation.}$$
$$4a = 24$$
$$\frac{4a}{4} = \frac{24}{4} \quad \textit{Divide each side by 4.}$$
$$a = 6 \quad \text{A check will show that the solution is 6.}$$

Example 2 Solve $\dfrac{y + 8}{6} = 3$.

$$\frac{y + 8}{6} = 3$$
$$\frac{y + 8}{6} \cdot 6 = 3 \cdot 6 \quad \textit{To undo division by 6, multiply both sides by 6.}$$
$$y + 8 = 18$$
$$y + 8 - 8 = 18 - 8 \quad \textit{Subtract 8 from each side.}$$
$$y = 10 \quad \text{A check will show that the solution is 10.}$$

State the steps you would use to solve each of the following equations.

1. $2x - 6 = 16$
2. $3x - 6 = 18$
3. $4(x + 3) = 4$
4. $6(n + 3) = 36$
5. $7x - 3 = 5$
6. $5x + 10 = 14$
7. $\frac{n}{4} + 6 = 16$
8. $\frac{x}{2} - 9 = 14$
9. $\frac{n - 7}{3} = 18$
10. $\frac{c + 5}{8} = 6$

11–20. Solve each equation in exercises 1–10.

Solve each of the following.

21. $-2t - 7 = -21$
22. $-11 = 4 + \frac{y}{-3}$
23. $6 = \frac{r + 8}{7}$
24. $\frac{4d + 20}{8} = 8$
25. $\frac{p}{-7} + 1 = 7$
26. $14 = 2x - 6$
27. $\frac{5x - 10}{5} = 7$
28. $-2x + 5 = 29$
29. $\frac{4 - x}{8} = 6$
30. $\frac{s - 8}{-4} = 28$

2.3 Simplifying Equations

Ralph Johnson earned $5 per hour working part-time. He worked 3 hours on Tuesday and 4 hours on Saturday. How much did he earn?

Method 1

He worked 3 hours Tuesday and 4 hours Saturday.
He worked $3 + 4$ or 7 hours altogether at $5 per hour.
$$(3 + 4)5 = 7 \cdot 5 \text{ or } 35$$
He earned $35 all together.

Method 2

He earned $3 \cdot 5$ or $15 on Tuesday.
He earned $4 \cdot 5$ or $20 on Saturday.
$$3 \cdot 5 + 4 \cdot 5 = 15 + 20 \text{ or } 35$$
He earned $35 all together.

You can see that $(3 + 4)5 = 3 \cdot 5 + 4 \cdot 5$. Ralph's part-time job was distributed between two days' work. This example shows a property of numbers called the **distributive property**.

Many rules or properties in algebra can be expressed in a general way by using several variables to represent numbers. Study the general statement of the distributive property.

> **For any numbers, *a*, *b*, and *c*,**
> $a(b + c) = ab + ac$ and $(b + c)a = ba + ca$.

Example 1 Use the distributive property to find the product $x(5 + y)$.

$$x(5 + y) = 5x + xy$$

In the expression $5x + xy$, $5x$ and xy are called **terms**. A term may be a product such as $5x$ and xy. But a term of an expression may also be a number such as -12 or a quotient such as $\frac{6}{a}$.

In the expression $8y + 5y - 12$, $8y$ and $5y$ are called **like terms** since they contain the same variable factor to the same power.

Examples 2 and 3 show how the distributive property is used to combine like terms.

Example 2 Simplify $8y + 5y - 12$.

$8y + 5y - 12 = (8 + 5)y - 12$ *Combine like terms by adding the coefficients.*
$\qquad\qquad\quad = 13y - 12$ *Notice that $13y$ and -12 are unlike terms so they cannot be combined.*

Example 3 Solve $4a - 6a + 8 = 0$.

$4a - 6a + 8 = 0$ *Like terms may be combined by subtraction.*
$(4 - 6) + 8 = 0$ *Simplify the expression on the left*
$\qquad -2a + 8 = 0$ *by using the distributive property.*
$\qquad\qquad -2a = -8$ *Subtract 8 from each side of the equation.*
$\qquad\qquad\quad a = \frac{-8}{-2}$ *Divide each side by -2.*
$\qquad\qquad\quad a = 4$ *A check will show that the solution is 4.*

13

In example 3 we simplified the left side of the equation before solving it. In any solution, you should look for ways to simplify each side of the equation.

An equation containing fractions may be simplified by multiplying each side by the least common denominator (LCD). Consider the following example.

Example 4   Solve $\frac{x}{2} + \frac{x}{3} = \frac{25}{6}$.

$$\frac{x}{2} + \frac{x}{3} = \frac{25}{6} \qquad \text{\textit{The LCD is 6.}}$$

$$6\left(\frac{x}{2} + \frac{x}{3}\right) = 6\left(\frac{25}{6}\right) \qquad \text{\textit{Multiply each side by the LCD, 6.}}$$

$$\frac{6x}{2} + \frac{6x}{3} = \frac{6(25)}{6} \qquad \text{\textit{Use the distributive property on the left.}}$$

$$3x + 2x = 25 \qquad \text{\textit{Reduce each fraction. Notice that this process eliminates the denominators.}}$$

$$5x = 25 \qquad \text{\textit{Combine like terms.}}$$

$$x = 5 \qquad \text{\textit{Solve by dividing each side by 5.}}$$

Check.

$$\frac{5}{2} + \frac{5}{3} \overset{?}{=} \frac{25}{6}$$

$$\frac{15}{6} + \frac{10}{6} \overset{?}{=} \frac{25}{6}$$

$$\frac{25}{6} = \frac{25}{6} \qquad \text{\textit{The solution is 5.}}$$

Find each product.

1. $7(a + b)$ **2.** $(a + c)2$ **3.** $3(x - y)$ **4.** $10(c - 7)$

5. $b(a + 18)$ **6.** $m(n + p)$ **7.** $(7 - 7a)5$ **8.** $8(3b + 6)$

Simplify each of the following expressions.

9. $19t + 2t$ **10.** $7x + 8x$ **11.** $2m + 17m$

12. $2x + (-7x) + 3x$ **13.** $3x + (-2x) + 2x$ **14.** $2(3b + 6b + 2b)$

15. $10y + 3y - 7y$ **16.** $13r - 16r + 11s$ **17.** $11w + 8 - 8w$

Solve each equation.

18. $3n + 2n = 45$ **19.** $9x - 3x = 36$ **20.** $20 = 19x + x$

21. $14 + 24x + 4x = 0$ **22.** $11y - 2y - 45 = 0$ **23.** $16 = 8r - 3r - 4$

24. $7y = 50 - 3y$ **25.** $a + 2a - 33 = 0$ **26.** $\frac{y}{5} + \frac{y}{7} = 12$

27. $\frac{4x + 5}{6} - \frac{x + 7}{4} = 2$ **28.** $\frac{x}{9} + \frac{x - 3}{6} = 27$ **29.** $\frac{c}{5} + \frac{c}{2} = 14$

30. $5x + 12 = 8x$ **31.** $\frac{3y}{4} - \frac{y}{3} = -5$ **32.** $\frac{a}{5} + \frac{a}{3} = 2$

2.4 Formulas

Sometimes rules or properties in algebra can be stated using equations composed of **several** variables. An example that you have met is the general statement of the distributive property. Another example is the **formula** $A = \ell w$. This equation expresses the relationship between the area (A) and the length (ℓ) and width (w) of a rectangle.

Suppose you know values for all the variables but one in a formula. Then, substitute those values in the formula and solve for the variable you do not know.

Example 1 Use $F = \frac{9}{5}C + 32$ to find the temperature on the Fahrenheit scale (F) that corresponds to 20° Celsius (C).

$$F = \frac{9}{5}C + 32$$
$$F = \frac{9}{5}(20) + 32 \qquad \textit{Substitute 20 for C in the formula.}$$
$$F = \frac{180}{5} + 32$$
$$F = 36 + 32 \text{ or } 68$$

A temperature of 68°F corresponds to 20°C.

Find the temperature that corresponds to each of the following. Use $F = \frac{9}{5}C + 32$.

1. 15°C
2. −20°C
3. 68°F
4. 0°C
5. 100°C

6. Find the distance (d) traveled in 2 hours (t) at a constant rate (r) of 55 miles per hour. Use $d = rt$.

7. Find the perimeter (p) of a square if the length of each side (s) is 17 inches. Use $p = 4s$.

8. Find the perimeter (p) of a triangle if the length of the sides (a, b, and c) are 4.5 centimeters, 4.2 centimeters, and 5.3 centimeters. Use $p = a + b + c$.

9. Find the interest (i) on $700 ($p$) for six months ($t$). The interest rate ($r$) is 3% per month. Use $i = prt$.

10. Find the interest on $900 invested for 2 years at a rate of $4\frac{3}{4}$%.

11. Find the interest on $1600 invested for 3 years at a rate of $5\frac{1}{2}$%.

12. Find the interest on $1800 invested for 3 years at a rate of $7\frac{1}{4}$%.

13. Find the distance (s) an object falls in 4 seconds (t) with an acceleration (g) of 32 feet per second.[2] Use $s = \frac{gt^2}{2}$.

14. A triangle has a base (b) of 30 inches and a height (h) of 8 inches. Find the area of the triangle. Use $A = \frac{bh}{2}$.

2.5 Solving Formulas for Specific Variables

Compare the methods used to solve for x in examples 1 and 2. Note that the equations have the same form.

Example 1 Solve $3x + 5 = 26$.

$$3x + 5 = 26$$
$$3x + 5 - 5 = 26 - 5$$
$$3x = 21$$
$$\frac{3x}{3} = \frac{21}{3}$$
$$x = 7$$

Example 2 Solve $ax + c = d$ for x.

$$ax + c = d$$
$$ax + c - c = d - c$$
$$ax = d - c$$
$$\frac{ax}{a} = \frac{d - c}{a}$$
$$x = \frac{d - c}{a}$$

To solve for one variable in a formula in terms of the other variables, use the methods of solving an equation with a single variable.

It often is more convenient to use a formula in a changed form. Suppose you must convert several temperatures from the Fahrenheit scale to the Celsius. in example 3 we find a handy formula for this situation.

Example 3 Solve $F = \frac{9}{5}C + 32$ for C.

$$F = \frac{9}{5}C + 32$$

$$F - 32 = \frac{9}{5}C \qquad \text{To undo multiplication by } \frac{9}{5}, \text{ divide by } \frac{9}{5}.$$

$$\frac{5}{9}(F - 32) = \frac{5}{9} \cdot \frac{9}{5}C \qquad \text{Notice that multipying by } \frac{5}{9} \text{ produces}$$

$$\frac{5}{9}(F - 32) = C \qquad \qquad \text{the same results as dividing by } \frac{9}{5}.$$

You can use the formula $C = \frac{5}{9}(F - 32)$ to find C when you know F.

Find the temperature that corresponds to each of the following. Use $C = \frac{5}{9}(F - 32)$.

1. $59°F$ 2. $-13°F$ 3. $32°F$ 4. $98.6°F$ 5. $77°F$

6. Find the rate Chandler travels if he drives 180 miles in 4 hours.

7. The formula $d = rt$ relates the distance (d) traveled by an object moving at a constant rate (r) in an interval of time (t). Solve for r in terms of d and t in the formula.

Solve each of the following equations for x.

8. $3x - 4n = m$ 9. $x + by = 3by$ 10. $t + x = s$

11. $\frac{cx}{2} + pt = r$ 12. $bx = a$ 13. $tx + 3cd = 4tx$

14. $abx + 2abx = 14$ 15. $ar + as + tx = 5$ 16. $9x + 2a = 2x + 9a$

CHAPTER TWO   SOLUTIONS and ANSWERS

Section 2.1

1. Add 22

2. Add 7

3. Subtract 5

4. Divide by 6

5. Divide by -9

6. Add -15

7. Multiply by 3

8. Multiply by -7

9. Add 2

10. Subtract -1

11. Divide by -3

12. Multiply by 5

13.
$$d - 7 = 12$$
$$d - 7 + 7 = 2 + 7$$
$$d = 19$$

14.
$$c - 3 = 1$$
$$c - 3 + 3 = 1 + 3$$
$$c = 4$$

15.
$$n + 6 = 25$$
$$n + 6 - 6 = 2 - 6$$
$$n = 19$$

16.
$$x + 17 = 47$$
$$x + 17 - 17 = 47 - 17$$
$$x = 30$$

17.
$$b - (-7) = -1$$
$$b - (-7) + (-7) = -1 + (-7)$$
$$b = -8$$

18.
$$m - (-2) = -5$$
$$m - (-2) + (-2) = -5 + (-2)$$
$$m = -7$$

19.
$$b + -2 = 38$$
$$b + (-2) - (-2) = 38 - (-2)$$
$$b = 40$$

20.
$$\frac{k}{7} = 11$$
$$\frac{k}{7} \cdot 7 = 11 \cdot 7$$
$$k = 77$$

21.
$$\frac{n}{5} = 20$$
$$\frac{n}{5} \cdot 5 = 20 \cdot 5$$
$$n = 100$$

22.
$$w + (-15) = -15$$
$$w + (-15) - (-15) = -15 - (-15)$$
$$w = 0$$

23. $x = 6$

24. $x = 14$

25. $u = -57$

26. $t = 90$

27. $t = -11$

28. $y = 18$

29. $m = 30$

30. $r = 16$

31. $x = 120$

32. $n = 26$

33. $c = -10$

34. $r = -48$

35. $n = 133$

36. $t = -11$

37. $n = 19$

38. $x = -17$

39. $w = 17$

40. $y = 5$

41. $r = \frac{1}{9}$

42. $j = 44$

43. $x = 4$

44. $m = 2\frac{1}{4}$

45. $x = 6.6$

Section 2.2

1. Add 6 to both sides, divide both sides by 2.

2. Add 6 to both sides, divide both sides by 3.

3. Divide both sides by 4, subtract 3 from both sides.

4. Divide both sides by 6, subtract 3 from both sides.

5. Add 3 to both sides, divide both sides by 7.

6. Subtract 10 from both sides, divide both sides by 5.

7. Subtract 6 from both sides, multiply both sides by 4.

8. Add 9 to both sides, multiply both sides by 2.

9. Multiply both sides by 3, add 7 to both sides.

10. Multiply both sides by 8, subtract 5 from both sides.

11.
$$2x - 6 = 16$$
$$2x = 22$$
$$x = 11$$

12.
$$3x - 6 = 18$$
$$3x = 24$$
$$x = 8$$

13.
$$4(x + 3) = 4$$
$$x + 3 = 1$$
$$x = -2$$

14.
$$6(n + 3) = 6$$
$$n + 3 = 6$$
$$n = 3$$

15.
$$7x - 3 = 5$$
$$7x = 8$$
$$x = \frac{8}{7} \text{ or } 1\frac{1}{7}$$

16.
$$5x + 10 = 14$$
$$5x = 4$$
$$x = \frac{4}{5}$$

17.
$$\frac{n}{4} + 6 = 16$$
$$\frac{n}{4} = 10$$
$$n = 40$$

18.
$$\frac{x}{2} - 9 = 14$$
$$\frac{x}{2} = 23$$
$$x = 46$$

19.
$$\frac{n-7}{3} = 18$$
$$n - 7 = 54$$
$$n = 61$$

20. $c = 43$ **21.** $t = 7$ **22.** $y = 45$ **23.** $r = 34$ **24.** $d = 11$

25. $p = -42$ **26.** $x = 10$ **27.** $x = 9$ **28.** $x = -12$ **29.** $x = -44$

30. $s = -104$

Section 2.3

1. $7a + 7b$

2. $2a + 2c$

3. $3x - 3y$

4. $10c - 70$

5. $ab + 18b$

6. $mn + mp$

7. $35 - 35a$

8. $24b + 48$

9. $19t + 2t = (19 + 2)t = 21t$

10. $7x + 8x = (7 + 8)x$
$= 15x$

11. $2m + 17m = (2 + 17)m$
$= 19m$

12. $2x + -7x + 3 = (2 + -7 + 3)x$
$= -2x$

13. $3x + -2x + 2x = (3 + -2 + 2)x$
$= 3x$

14. $2(3b + 6b + 2b) = 6b + 12b + 4b$
$= (6 + 12 + 4)b$
$= 22b$

15. $10y + 3y - 7y = (10 + 3 - 7)y$
$= 6y$

16. $13r - 16r + 11s = 11s - 3r$

17. $11w + 8 - 8w = (11 - 8)w + 8$
$= 3w + 8$

18. $3n + 2n = 45$
$(3 + 2)n = 45$
$5n = 45$
$n = \dfrac{45}{5}$
$n = 9$

19. $9x - 3x = 36$
$(9 - 3)x = 36$
$6x = 36$
$x = \dfrac{36}{6}$
$x = 6$

20. $20 = 19x + x$
$20 = (19 + 1)x$
$20 = 20x$
$\dfrac{20}{20} = x$
$1 = x$

21. $x = \dfrac{-1}{2}$

22. $y = 5$

23. $r = 4$

24. $y = 5$

25. $a = 11$

26. $y = 35$

27. $x = 7$

28. $x = 99$

29. $c = 20$

30. $x = 4$

31. $y = -12$

32. $a = \dfrac{15}{4}$

Section 2.4

For exercises 1 - 5, $F = \dfrac{9}{5}C + 32$.

1. $F = \dfrac{9}{5}(15) + 32$
$F = 27 + 32$
$F = 59;\ 59°\ F$

2. $F = \dfrac{9}{5}(-20) + 32$
$F = 9(-4) + 32$
$F = -36 + 32$
$F = -4;\ -4°\ F$

3. $68 = \dfrac{9}{5}C + 32$
$68 - 32 = \dfrac{9}{5}C$
$36 = \dfrac{9}{5}C$
$36 \div \dfrac{9}{5} = C$
$36 \cdot \dfrac{5}{9} = C$
$20 = C;\ 20°C$

4. $F = \dfrac{9}{5}(0) + 32$
$F = 0 + 32$
$F = 32;\ 32°\ F$

5. $F = \dfrac{9}{5}(100) + 32$
$F = 9(20) + 32$
$F = 180 + 32$
$F = 212;\ 212°\ F$

6. $d = rt$
$d = 2 \cdot 55$
$d = 110;\ 110$ miles

7. $p = 4s$
$p = 4 \cdot 17$
$p = 68;\ 68$ in.

8. $p = a + b + c$
$p = 4.5 + 4.2 + 5.3$
$p = 14.0;\ 14$ cm

9. $i = prt$
$i = 700(0.03)(6)$
$i = 126;\ \$126$

10. $i = prt$
$i = 900(0.0475)(2)$
$i = 85.5;\ \$85.50$

11. $i = prt$
$i = 1600(0.055)(3)$
$i = 264;\ \$264$

12. $i = prt$
$i = 1800(0.0725)(3)$
$i = 391.5;\ \$391.50$

13. $s = \dfrac{gt^2}{2}$
$s = \dfrac{32(4)^2}{2}$
$s = 256;\ 256$ ft

14. $A = \dfrac{bh}{2}$
$A = \dfrac{30 \cdot 8}{2}$
$A = \dfrac{240}{2}$
$A = 120;\ 120$ in.^{2}

Section 2.5

In exercises 1 - 5, $C = \frac{5}{9}(F - 32)$.

1. $C = 15$ **2.** $C = -25$ **3.** $C = 0$ **4.** $C = 37$ **5.** $C = 25$

6. 45 mph   **7.** $r = \frac{d}{t}$ **8.** $x = \frac{m + 4n}{3}$ **9.** $x = 2by$ **10.** $x = s - t$

11. $x = \frac{2r - 2pt}{c}$ **12.** $x = \frac{a}{b}$ **13.** $y = \frac{cd}{t}$ **14.** $x = \frac{14}{3ab}$ **15.** $y = \frac{5 - ar - as}{t}$

16. $x = a$

CHAPTER 3   SOLVING PROBLEMS

3.1   Writing Equations

Algebraic equations are useful in solving many verbal problems. Solve verbal sentences about equal quantities are translated into equations in the following table.

Verbal Sentence	Equation
A number increased by 5 is 11.	$n + 5 = 11$
Six more than a number equals 8.	$6 + m = 8$
A number reduced by 2 is 108.	$k - 2 = 108$
Sixteen diminished by a number is 4.	$16 - b = 4$
Eight multiplied times a number is 48.	$8x = 48$
One-fourth of a number is 22.	$\frac{1}{4}y = 22$
The quotient of 2.5 and a number equals 5.	$\frac{2.5}{d} = 5$

In the table different variables represent the unknown numbers in the sentences.

Example 1   Define a variable and write an equation for the sentence.

One-half of a number decreased by 7 is 33.

Define a variable.   Let x = the number.

Write an equation.

One-half	times	a number	decreased by	7	equals	33.
$\frac{1}{2}$	$\cdot$	x	$-$	7	$=$	33

Example 2   Pat paid $13 for material for a dress at $3.25 a yard. Define a variable and write an equation to find the number of yards she bought.

Define a variable.   Let y = the number of yards of material Pat bought.

Write an equation.

$3.25	times	the number of yards	equals	$13.
3.25	$\cdot$	y	$=$	13

Write an equation for each of the following.

1. The difference of w and 2 is 9.

2. The product of b and 4 is 25.

3. The quotient of 11 and k is 8.

4. One-sixth of j is 10.

5. Eight less a number is 5.

6. The sum of n and 6 is 17.

For each of the following sentences, define a variable and write an equation.

7. A number divided by 5 is 10.

8. Nine less a number is the same number.

9. Nine plus some number is 10.

10. Twice a number plus 2 is 20.

11. Three times the sum of 2 and some number is 78.

12. When 7 is subtracted from the product of a number and 4, the result is 8.

Define a variable and write an equation to solve each problem.

13. The round-trip fare for a bus trip is $53. Spencer spent $87 for food and the fare. How much did Spencer spend for food?

14. Seven stereo tapes cost $63. Each tape costs the same. How much does each tape cost?

15. A sandwich and soup sell for $3.79. The soup is $1.59. How much is the sandwich?

3.2 Solving Verbal Problems

Verbal problems are solved using the following five steps.

1. Read the problem carefully to determine what quantity is to be found. *Define a variable* to stand for that quantity.

2. *Write an equation* from the relationship of the variable to the known facts.

3. *Solve the equation.*

4. Always *check the solution* with the words of the problem.

5. *Answer the problem* in words.

Example 1 The greater of two numbers is twice the lesser number. If the greater number is decreased by 12, the result is 1 more than the lesser number. Find the two numbers.

1. Define a variable.   Let x = the lesser number.
                                      Then $2x$ = the greater number.

2. Write an equation.

The greater number	decreased by	12	equals	1	more than	the lesser number.
$2x$	$-$	12	$=$	1	$+$	x

3. Solve the equation.
$$2x - 12 = 1 + x$$
$$2x - x - 12 = 1 \qquad \textit{Subtract x from each side.}$$
$$x = 1 + 12 \qquad \textit{Add 12 to each side.}$$
$$x = 13$$
$$\text{Then } 2x = 26.$$

4. Check the solution.   The greater number, 26, decreased by 12 is 14.
                                    One more than the lesser number is 1 + 13 or 14.
                                    Since 14 = 14, the solution checks.

5. Answer the problem. The two numbers are 26 and 13.

Consecutive numbers are numbers in counting order, such as 3, 4, 5. Recall that the integers are the numbers ..., –3, –2, –1, 0, 1, 2, 3 ... The integers are given in consecutive order in the preceding list.

An **even** integer is an integer that is divided exactly by 2. Thus, three consecutive even integers are 4, 6, 8. Another example is –10, –8, –6.

Odd integers are not divisible by 2. Examples of consecutive odd integers are –7, –5, –3 and 47, 49, 51.

22

Example 2   The sum of three consecutive integers is 102. Find the integers.

Define a variable.

Let x = the least integer.
Then $x + 1$ = the next integer. *An integer increased by 1 is the next consecutive integer.*
And $x + 2$ = the greatest integer (of the three).

Write an equation.

The sum of three consecutive integers equals 102.
$$x + (x + 1) + (x + 2) \qquad = \qquad 102.$$

Solve the equation.

$$x + x + 1 + x + 2 = 102$$
$$3x + 3 = 102 \qquad \text{\textit{Combine like terms.}}$$
$$3x = 102 - 3 \quad \text{\textit{Subtract 3 from each side.}}$$
$$3x = 99$$
$$\frac{3x}{3} = \frac{99}{3} \qquad \text{\textit{Divide each side by 3.}}$$
$$x = 33$$
Then $x + 1 = 34$ and
$$x + 2 = 35$$

Check the solution.

Are 33 + 34 + 35 equal to 102?
Since 102 = 102, the solution checks.

Answer the problem.

The three integers are 33, 34, and 35.

Example 3   The sum of three consecutive even integers is 90. Find the integers.

Define a variable.

Let $2x$ = the least even integer.   *The variable x may be odd or even, but 2x is always even.*
Then $2x + 2$ = the next even integer.
And $2x + 4$ = the greatest even integer.

Write an equation.

The sum of three consecutive even integers equals 90.
$$2x + (2x + 2) + (2x + 4) = 90$$

Solve the equation.

$$2x + 2x + 2 + 2x + 4 = 90$$
$$6x + 6 = 90$$
$$6x = 90 - 6$$
$$\frac{6x}{6} = \frac{84}{6}$$
$$x = 14$$

The least even integer = $2x$
$$2x = 2 \cdot 14 = 28$$

Next even integer = $2x + 2$
$$2(14) + 2 = 30$$

Greatest even integer = $2x + 4$
$$2(14) + 4 = 32$$

Check the solution.

Are 28 + 30 + 32 $\overset{?}{=}$ 90?
$$90 = 90$$

Answer the problem.

The three consecutive even integers are 28, 30, and 32.

23

Suppose x represents a number in each of the following. Name the numbers in each exercise.

1. a number and the number increased by 22

2. two consecutive even integers

3. four consecutive even integers

4. three consecutive odd integers (Since an even number is $2x$, then an odd number is $2x + 1$.)

5. a number and its double

6. three consecutive integers

7. a number and the number decreased by 12

8. two numbers whose sum is 45

For each problem define a variable. Then write and solve an equation.

9. The difference of two integers is 2. The greater integer is 5. What is the other integer?

10. The sum two integers is –7. One of the integers is 3. Find the other integer.

11. The sum of two integers is –10. One of the integers is 1. Find the other integer.

12. Five times the sum of a number and 4 equals fifty. Find the number.

13. The product of 4 and a number is 24. Find the number.

14. Some number increased by 9 is 41. What is the number?

15. Find two consecutive integers whose sum is 99.

16. Find two consecutive integers such that the sum of the greater integer and three times the lesser integer is 65.

17. The sum of two numbers is 72. The greater number is twice the lesser. Find the numbers.

18. Find two consecutive even integers whose sum is 46.

19. Find two consecutive integers whose sum is 27.

20. Find three consecutive odd integers whose sum is –81.

21. Find three consecutive even integers such that three times the middle integer is 10 more than the greatest.

22. Find the three consecutive even integers whose sum is –96.

23. Find two numbers whose sum is 55 if the greater is four times the lesser.

24. Find two consecutive even integers such that the lesser is two times the greater.

25. Find two consecutive odd integers whose sum is 196.

26. Find three consecutive even integers whose sum is 0.

3.3 Problems Involving Money

Many verbal problems involve sums of money as well as percents. Study the way that percents and decimals are handled in the following example.

Example 1   It costs the Wodge Company $1.71 to manufacture a wodgit. What should the selling price of a wodgit be if the company is to make a profit of 5%?

Define a variable.   Let x = the selling price of each wodgit.
Then 5% $\cdot$ x or $0.05x$ = the amount of profit on each wodgit.

Write an equation.

The cost to manufacture a wodgit	plus	the amount of profit	is	the selling price.
1.71	+	0.05x	=	x

Solve the equation.
$$1.71 + 0.05x = x$$
$$1.71 = x - 0.05x$$
$$1.71 = (1 - 0.05)x$$
$$1.71 = 0.95x$$
$$\frac{1.71}{0.95} = x$$
$$1.8 = x$$

Check the answer.   If the selling price is $1.80, the amount of profit is 5% of 1.80 or $0.05 \cdot 1.80$. This is $0.09. The manufacturing cost, $1.71, plus the profit, $0.09, is $1.80, the selling price.

Answer the problem.   The price of each wodgit should be $1.80.

For each of the following, define a variable and write and solve an equation.

1. Each member of a photograph club contributes $7.00 to buy film. There are 14 members. How much money is contributed to buy film?

2. A coat originally cost $68. For a special sale, the coat is reduced by $22. What is the sale price?

3. Sam earns $6.75 per hour. Last week he worked 30 hours. How much did he earn?

4. Clark bought 2 hamburgers and Phil bought 5 hamburgers. Together they spent $5.25. If each of the hamburgers was the same price, find the price of one hamburger.

5. Twelve members of a club pay dues of $6.50 per person. How much money is collected in dues?

6. Jordan receives a 3% commission on each house he sells. If he sells a house for $75,000, what is his commission?

7. Joanna and Collin together spent $48 for compact discs. Joanna bought 3 and Collin bought 1. Each of the CDs was the same price. How much was each?

8. The original price of a television set was $460. What is the sale price if it is marked down 25%?

9. The Ajax Company can sell gidgets for $10.97 a piece. What does it cost the company to manufacture each gidget if it makes a profit of 8%?

10. A store advertises an air conditioner on sale for $280. If this is marked down 20%, what was the original price?

3.4 Formulas in Problems

Sometimes you can use a formula to derive an equation for a verbal problem.

Example 1 The perimeter of a rectangle is 26 feet. The length is 2 feet less than 4 times the width. Find the width and length of the rectangle.

Look at the sketch at the right. Can you see why the formula for the perimeter of a rectangle is $p = 2w + 2\ell$?

Define a variable.
Let $x = w$, the width of the rectangle.
Then $4x - 2 = \ell$, the length of the rectangle.

Write an equation.
Use $p = 2w + 2\ell$.
$$26 = 2x + 2(4x - 2)$$
$$26 = 2x + 8x - 4$$

Solve the equation.
$$26 = 2x + 8x - 4$$
$$26 + 4 = 10x$$
$$30 = 10x$$
$$3 = x$$
Then $4x - 2 = 4 \cdot 3 - 2$ or 10.

Check the solution.
Substituting in the formula for the perimeter of a rectangle, you find that $2(3) + 2(10) = 6 + 20$ or 26. The perimeter is 26 feet.

Answer the problem.
The width is 3 feet and the length is 10 feet.

Example 2 Two airplanes take off at the same time from an airport. One flies west at a constant rate of 800 km/h. The other flies east at a constant rate of 1000 km/h. In how many hours will they be 9000 km apart?

Define a variable.
Let h = the number of hours until the airplanes are 9000 km apart. It may be helpful to draw a sketch. Use the formula that relates distance traveled to the rate and time of travel, $d = rt$.

Westbound plane's distance   Eastbound plane's distance
$800 \cdot h$ + $1000 \cdot h$ Use $d = rt$

9000 km

Write an equation.
The westbound plus the eastbound is the total
plane's distance   plane's distance   distance.
$800h$ + $1000h$ =   9000

Solve the equation.
$$1800h = 9000$$
$$h = \frac{9000}{1800}$$
$$h = 5$$

Check the solution.   Since $d = rt$, the westbound plane flies 800 · 5 or 4000 km.
The eastbound plane flies 1000 · 5 or 5000 km. After 5 hours,
the planes are 4000 + 5000 or 9000 km apart.

Answer the problem.   In 5 hours, the planes will be 9000 km apart.

For each of the following, define a variable. Then write and solve an equation.

1. A triangle that has two sides with the same measure is isosceles. Suppose the third side of an isosceles triangle is 5 cm longer than each of the other sides and the perimeter is 26 cm. Find the lengths of the three sides.

2. The length of a rectangular room is 8 m less than two times its width. Its perimeter is 50 m. Find its dimensions.

3. The length of a soccer field is 75 yards less than 3 times its width. Its perimeter is 370 yards. Find its dimensions.

4. The perimeter of a triangle is 12 cm. If the measures of the three sides are consecutive numbers, find the length of the three sides.

5. Trevor drove 4 hours at a rate of 50 mph. How long would the same distance take Trevor if he drove at 40 mph?

6. Luke leaves school at the same time as Jessica. Luke drives 5 mph faster than Jane. After 3 hours of driving in opposite directions, they are 201 miles apart. How fast is Luke driving?

7. Robert inherited $4000 from his grandmother. Part was invested at 5% while the rest was invested at $6\frac{1}{2}$%. The total interest for a year was $227. How much was invested at $6\frac{1}{2}$%?

8. As treasurer, Anthony decided to invest $600 collected in club dues. Part was invested in a 3% account for immediate access with the rest in a long term $7\frac{1}{4}$% account. If the interest for 1 year was $26.50, how much was invested at $7\frac{1}{4}$%?

9. Allison invested $2200 in two banks. At the first bank she had an interest rate of $4\frac{1}{2}$% and at the second bank the interest rate was $5\frac{3}{4}$%. If the interest obtained at the end of the year was $107.75, how much money was invested at $5\frac{3}{4}$%?

10. Min leaves the house traveling 28 mph in her car. She overtakes Lew in 2 hours. Lew is riding his bicycle and left the house 5 hours before Min. How fast is Lew traveling?

3.5 Mixture and Work Problems

Many people work with mixtures in their jobs or in everyday situations.

Example 1   A chemist has 6 liters of a 25% alcohol solution. How much water must she add so that the resulting solution contains 20% alcohol?

Define a variable.   Let x = the amount of water added. A chart is a convenient way to organize the information in this situation.

	Total Amount (L)	Amount of Alcohol (L)
25% solution	6	0.25(6)
20% solution	6 + x	0.20(6 + x)

Since water is added, the amount of alcohol in each solution will be the same.

Write an equation.

The amount of alcohol in the 25% solution	is	the amount of alcohol in the 20% solution.
0.25(6)	=	0.20(6 + x)

Solve the equation.

$$1.5 = 1.2 + 0.20x$$
$$1.5 - 1.2 = 0.20x$$
$$0.3 = 0.20x$$
$$\frac{0.3}{0.20} = x$$
$$1.5 = x$$

Check the solution.   The amount of alcohol in 6 liters of the 25% solution is 1.5 liters. If the chemist adds 1.5 liters of water to 6 liters, she then has 7.5 liters of which 20% is alcohol. That is, 0.20(7.5) or 1.5 liters is alcohol. Since the amount of alcohol remains the same, the solution checks.

Answer the problem.   The chemist must add 1.5 liters of water.

In distance problems, rate refers to the distance traveled per unit time. You are familiar with the formula, $d = rt$.

Similarly, in work problems, rate refers to the work done per unit time. This idea can be expressed in a formula.

(work done)	=	(rate of work)	·	(time)
w	=	r	·	t

Martha wishes to paint her living room. She can paint the room in 3 hours. Thus, she can paint $\frac{1}{3}$ of the room is 1 hour. Her rate of work is $\frac{1}{3}$ of the job per hour. In t hours, Martha can paint $\frac{1}{3}t$ of the entire room.

Example 2 Suppose David can paint Martha's living room in 4 hours. How long will it take Martha and David to paint the room if they work together?

David's rate of painting is $\frac{1}{4}$ of the job per hour. In t hours, David can paint $\frac{1}{4}t$ of the room.

Define a variable.   Let t = the number of hours it takes Martha and David to paint the room if they work together.

Write an equation.

The part of the room Martha paints	plus	the part of the room David paints	is	1 room painted.
$\frac{1}{3}t$	+	$\frac{1}{4}t$	=	1

Solve the equation.

$$\left(\frac{1}{3}+\frac{1}{4}\right)t = 1$$

The LCD of the fractions is 12. $\left(\frac{4}{12}+\frac{3}{12}\right)t = 1$

$$\frac{7}{12}t = 1$$
$$7t = 12$$
$$t = \frac{12}{7}$$

Check the solution.

Martha paints $\frac{1}{3}\cdot\frac{12}{7}$ or $\frac{4}{7}$ of the room in $\frac{12}{7}$ hours.

David paints $\frac{1}{4}\cdot\frac{12}{7}$ or $\frac{3}{7}$ of the room in $\frac{12}{7}$ hours.

Together they paint $\frac{4}{7}+\frac{3}{7}$ or 1 room. The solution checks.

Answer the problem.   Martha and David can paint the living room in $1\frac{5}{7}$ hours.

Solve each of the following problems.

1. A baker has a 30-pound mixture of flour and sugar which is 40% sugar. How much flour must be added to the mixture to make it 20% sugar?

2. A candymaker has 10 liters of a solution which is 25% sugar. How much water must be added to the solution to make it 20% sugar?

3. Suppose you have 4 liters of paint that is 60% green and 40% white. How much green paint must you add to produce a mixture that is 80% green and 20% white?

4. A chemist has 20 liters of a solution which is 35% salt. How much water must be added to make the solution 28% salt?

5. An oil tanker can be filled in 10 hours from one pipe. It can be filled by another pipe in 8 hours. How long will it take to fill the tanker using both pipes?

6. A gas storage tank can be filled from one pipeline in 7 hours and by another pipeline in 5 hours. How many hours will it take to fill the tank if both pipelines are used?

7. James can stuff 1000 envelopes in 5 hours. Susan can stuff 1000 envelopes in 3 hours. How long will it take to stuff 1000 envelopes if they work together?

8. A chemist has a solution that is 20% acid and 80% water. He adds 5 liters of water to make a solution that is 15% acid. What is the volume of the original solution?

3.6 Miscellaneous Problems

You can use the five steps to solve any type of verbal problem.

Example 1 Jerry has the same number of dimes as nickels in his pocket. He has $0.45 in his pocket. How many dimes has he?

Define a variable. Let x = the number of dimes Jerry has.
Then x = the number of nickels he has also.

Write an equation.

The amount of money of dimes	plus	the amount of money in nickels	is	$0.45.
$0.10 \cdot x$	+	$0.05 \cdot x$	=	0.45

Solve the equation.

$$0.10x + 0.05x = 0.45$$
$$0.15x = 0.45$$
$$x = \frac{0.45}{0.15}$$
$$x = 3$$

Check the solution. If Jerry has 3 dimes and 3 nickels he has $0.10 \cdot 3$ or $0.30 and $0.05 \cdot 3$ or $0.15. He has $0.45 all together.

Answer the problem. Jerry has three dimes.

Solve each of the following problems.

1. Holly's bowling handicap is 6 less than half her average. Her handicap is 62. What is Holly's bowling average?

2. Juan bought 3 ties and 2 pairs of socks for $78.50. If the price of each tie is $12 more than each pair of socks, find the cost of each.

3. The museum charges adults $5 and students $2.40 for tickets. If 70 more student than adult tickets are sold, how many of each kind are sold if ticket receipts are $922.80?

4. Last year Chad sold 8 minivans more than twice the number of trucks Elizabeth sold. Chad sold 124 minivans. How many trucks did Elizabeth sell?

5. Renee sold some stock for $92 a share. This was $50 a share more than twice what she paid for it. At what price did she buy the stock?

6. A coin bank contains 6 times more quarters than dimes. The total amount of money in the bank is $38.40. How many dimes and quarters are in the bank?

7. In a basketball game, the Bobcats scored twice as many field goals worth 2 points each as free throws worth 1 point each. If the Bobcats' final score was 75 points, how many of each kind of basket did they score?

8. Willie earns $6 an hour for the first 40 hours, then $9 an hour for overtime. How many hours must he work in order to make $375?

9. Almonds cost $1.60 per pound. Walnuts cost $1.10 per pound. How many pounds of each should be mixed to produce a 40 pound mixture at $1.25 per pound?

10. City Bank charges $2.60 a month plus 6¢ per check. How many checks may be written in a month for a total charge of $5?

CHAPTER 3   SOLUTIONS and ANSWERS

SECTION 3.1

1. $w - 2 = 9$

2. $4b = 25$

3. $\dfrac{11}{k} = 8$

4. $\dfrac{1}{6}j = 10$

5. $8 - a = 5$

6. $n + 6 = 17$

7. Let $x =$ the number.
$$\dfrac{x}{5} = 10$$

8. Let $x =$ the number.
$$9 - x = x$$

9. Let $x =$ the number.
$$9 + x = 10$$

10. Let $x =$ the number.
$$2x + 2 = 20$$

11. Let $x =$ the number.
$$3(2 + x) = 78$$

12. Let $x =$ the number.
$$4x - 7 = 8$$

13. Let $x =$ the amount Spencer spent for food.
$$x + 53 = 87$$

14. Let $x =$ the cost of each tape.
$$7x = 63$$

15. Let $x =$ the cost of the sandwich.
$$x + 1.59 = 3.79$$

Section 3.2

1. x and $x + 22$

2. $2x$ and $2x + 2$

3. $2x, 2x + 2, 2x + 4,$ and $2x + 6$

4. $2x + 1, 2x + 3,$ and $2x + 5$

5. x and $2x$

6. $x, x + 1,$ and $x + 2$

7. x and $x - 12$

8. x and $45 - x$

9. Let $x =$ the other integer.
$$5 - x = 2$$
$$-x = 2 - 5$$
$$-x = -3 \quad 5 - 3 \overset{?}{=} 2$$
$$x = 3 \qquad 2 = 2$$
The integer is 3.

10. Let $x =$ the other integer.
$$x + 3 = -7$$
$$x = -7 - 3$$
$$x = -10$$
$$-10 + 3 \overset{?}{=} -7$$
$$-7 = -7$$
The number is -10.

11. Let $x =$ the other integer.
$$x + 1 = -10$$
$$x = -10 - 1 \quad -11 + 1 \overset{?}{=} -10$$
$$x = -11 \qquad -10 = -10$$
The integer is -11.

12. Let $x =$ the number.
$$5(x + 4) = 50$$
$$5x + 20 = 50$$
$$5x = 50 - 20$$
$$\dfrac{5x}{5} = \dfrac{30}{5}$$
$$x = 6$$
$$5(6 + 4) \overset{?}{=} 50$$
$$50 = 50$$
The number is 6.

13. Let $x =$ the number.
$$4x = 24 \quad 4 \cdot 6 = 24$$
$$\dfrac{4x}{4} = \dfrac{24}{4} \quad 24 = 24$$
$$x = 6 \qquad$$ The number is 6.

14. Let $x =$ the number.
$$x + 9 = 41$$
$$x = 41 - 9$$
$$x = 32 \quad 32 + 9 \overset{?}{=} 41$$
$$41 = 41$$
The number 32.

15. $x = 49$, the integers are 49 and 50.

16. $x = 16$, the integers are 16 and 17.

17. $x = 24$, the numbers are 24 and 48.

18. $x = 11$, the integers are 22 and 24.

19. $x = 13$, the integers are 13 and 14.

20. $x = -15$, the integers are $-29, -27,$ and -25.

21. $x = 2$, the integers are 4, 6, and 8.

22. $x = -17$, the integers are $-34, -32,$ and -30.

23. $x = 11$, the numbers are 11 and 44.

24. $x = -2$, the integers are -4 and -2.

25. $x = 48$, the integers are 97 and 99.

26. $x = -1$, the integers are $-2, 0$ and 2.

Section 3.3

1. Let $x =$ the amount contributed.
   The amount contributed is the amount given by each times the number of members.
   $x = 7 \cdot 14$
   $x = 98$
   A total of $98 is contributed.

2. Let $x =$ the sale price.
   The sale price plus the reduction is the original price.
   $x + 22 = 68$
   $\quad x = 68 - 22$
   $\quad x = 46$
   The sale price is $46.

3. Let $x =$ the amount Sam earns.
   The total earnings is the pay per hour times the number of hours.
   $x = 6.75 \cdot 30$
   $x = 202.50$
   Sam earns $202.50.

4. Let $x =$ the price of one hamburger.
   The price of one hamburger is the total price divided by the number of hamburgers.
   $x = 5.25 \div (2 + 5)$
   $x = 5.25 \div 7$
   $x = \dfrac{5.25}{7}$
   $x = 0.75$
   Each hamburger is $0.75.

5. Let $x =$ the amount collected in dues.
   The total of dues is the dues per person times the number of members.
   $x = 6.5 \cdot 12$
   $x = 78$
   A total of $78 in dues is collected.

6. Let $x =$ the commission
   $x = 0.03(75,000)$
   $x = 2250$
   The commission is $2250.

7. Let $x =$ the price of a compact disc.
   $3x + x = 48$
   $\quad 4x = 48$
   $\quad\quad x = 12$
   Each CD is $12.

8. $x = 345$, the sale price is $345.

9. $x = 10.16$, the manufacturing cost is $10.16.

10. $x = 350$, the original cost was $350.

Section 3.4

1. Let $x =$ the length of each of the two equal sides.
   Then $x + 5 =$ the length of the 3rd side.
   The sides of the triangle have lengths of 7, 7, and 12 cm.

2. Let $w =$ the width of the room.
   Then $l = 2w - 8$
   $\quad P = 2l + 2w$
   $\quad 50 = 2(2w - 8) + 2w$
   $\quad 50 = 4w - 16 + 2w$
   $\quad 66 = 6w$
   $\quad 11 = w$
   Then $l = 2 \cdot 11 - 8$
   $\quad\quad l = 14$
   $\quad\quad 50 \overset{?}{=} 2 \cdot 14 + 2 \cdot 11$
   $\quad\quad 50 = 50$
   The width is 11 m and the length is 14 m.

3. Let w = the width of the field.
Then $l = 3w - 75$
$$P = 2l + 2w$$
$$370 = 2(3w - 75) + 2w$$
$$370 = 6w - 150 + 2w$$
$$520 = 8w$$
$$65 = w$$
Then $l = 3 \cdot 65 - 75$
$$l = 195 - 75$$
$$l = 120$$
$$370 \overset{?}{=} 2 \cdot 120 + 2 \cdot 65$$
$$370 \overset{?}{=} 240 + 130$$
$$370 = 370$$
The width is 65 yd and the length is 120 yd.

4. Let x = the length of one side.
Then $x + 1$ = the length of the 2nd side and
$x + 2$ = the length of the third side.
The triangle sides have lengths of 3, 4, and 5 cm.

5. Trevor would cover 200 miles in 5 hours.

6. Luke is driving 36 mph.

7. $1800 were invested at $6\frac{1}{2}\%$.

8. $200 were invested at $7\frac{1}{4}\%$.

9. $700 were invested at $5\frac{3}{4}\%$.

10. Lew is traveling 8 mph.

Section 3.5

1. Let x = amount of flour added.
Initial amount of sugar equals later amount of sugar.
$$0.40(30) = 0.20(30 + x)$$
$$12 = 6 + 0.2x$$
$$\frac{6}{0.2} = \frac{0.2x}{0.2}$$
$$30 = x$$
$$0.40(30) \overset{?}{=} 0.20(30 + 30)$$
$$12 \overset{?}{=} 6 + 6$$
$$12 = 12$$
30 lb of flour are added.

2. Let x = the amount of water added.
Amount of sugar initially equals amount of sugar later.
$$0.25(10) = 0.20(10 + x)$$
$$2.5 = 2 + 0.20x$$
$$\frac{0.5}{0.2} = \frac{0.20x}{0.2}$$
$$2.5 = x$$
$$0.25(10) \overset{?}{=} 0.20(10 + 2.5)$$
$$2.5 \overset{?}{=} 2 + 0.5$$
$$2.5 = 2.5$$
2.5 liters are added.

3. 4 liters of green paint are added.

4. 5 liters of water are added.

5. It will take $4\frac{4}{9}$ hours to fill the tanker using both pipes.

6. It will take $2\frac{11}{12}$ hours to fill the storage tank using both pipes.

7. It will take $1\frac{7}{8}$ hours to stuff 1,000 envelopes working together.

8. The original solution had 15 liters of water.

Section 3.6

1. Let x = Holly's bowling average.
   Then $\frac{1}{2}x - 6$ = her handicap.
   $$\frac{1}{2}x - 6 = 62$$
   $$\frac{1}{2}x = 68$$
   $$x = 136$$
   $$\frac{1}{2}(136) - 6 \stackrel{?}{=} 62$$
   $$68 - 6 \stackrel{?}{=} 62$$
   $$62 = 62$$
   Holly's bowling average is 136.

2. Let x = the cost of a pair of socks.
   Then $x + 12$ = the cost of a tie.
   $$3(x + 12) + 2x = 78.50$$
   $$3x + 36 + 2x = 78.50$$
   $$5x = 42.50$$
   $$x = \frac{42.50}{5}$$
   $$x = 8.50$$
   $$3(8.50 + 12) + 2(8.50) \stackrel{?}{=} 78.50$$
   $$25.50 + 36 + 17 \stackrel{?}{=} 78.50$$
   $$78.50 = 78.50$$
   Each pair of socks costs $8.50 and each tie costs $20.50.

3. Let x = the number of adult tickets.
   Then $x + 70$ = the number of student tickets.
   The value of the adult tickets plus the value of the student tickets equal $922.80.
   $$5x + 2.40(x + 70) = 922.80$$
   $$5x + 2.40x + 168 = 922.80$$
   $$7.4x + 168 = 922.8$$
   $$7.4x = 754.80$$
   $$x = 102$$
   $$5(102) + 2.40(102 + 70) \stackrel{?}{=} 922.80$$
   $$510 + 412.80 = 922.80$$
   $$922.80 = 922.80$$
   102 adult tickets and 172 student tickets were sold.

4. Let x = the number of trucks Elizabeth sold.
   Then $2x + 8$ = the number Chad sold.
   $$2x + 8 = 124$$
   $$2x = 116$$
   $$x = 58$$
   $$2(58) + 8 \stackrel{?}{=} 124$$
   $$116 + 8 \stackrel{?}{=} 124$$
   $$124 = 24$$
   Elizabeth sold 58 trucks.

5. Let x = the buying price of the stock.
   Then $2x + 50$ = selling price.
   $$2x + 50 = 92$$
   $$2x = 42$$
   $$x = 21$$
   $$2(21) + 50 \stackrel{?}{=} 42$$
   $$42 + 50 \stackrel{?}{=} 92$$
   $$92 = 92$$
   She bought the stock at $21 per share.

6. Let x = the number of dimes.
   Then $6x$ = the number of quarters.
   Value of dimes plus value of quarters equal total value.
   $$0.10(x) + 0.25(6x) = 38.40$$
   $$0.10x + 1.5x = 38.40$$
   $$1.6x = 38.40$$
   $$x = 24$$
   $$0.10(24) + 0.25(144) \stackrel{?}{=} 38.40$$
   $$2.4 + 36 \stackrel{?}{=} 38.40$$
   $$38.40 = 38.40$$
   There are 24 dimes and 144 quarters in the bank.

7. Let x = the number of free throws.
   Then $2x$ = the number of field goals.
   Field goal points plus free throw points equal total points.
   $$2(2x) + 1 \cdot x = 75$$
   $$4x + x = 75$$
   $$5x = 75$$
   $$x = 15$$
   $$2(2 \cdot 15) + 15 \stackrel{?}{=} 75$$
   $$2 \cdot 30 + 15 \stackrel{?}{=} 75$$
   $$75 = 75$$
   15 free throws and 30 field goals scored.

8. $x = 55$, Willie must work 55 hours.

9. $x = 12$, there are 12 pounds of almonds and 28 pounds of walnuts.

10. $x = 40$, forty checks can be written.

CHAPTER 4   MONOMIALS AND POLYNOMIALS

4.1   Adding Monomials

The following algebraic expressions are called **monomials**.

$$-7x^2 \qquad 15 \qquad y \qquad \frac{1}{2}x^3y^2$$

A specific number, such as 15, is called a **constant**. Notice that each monomial is a constant, variable, or product. Expressions such as $2x+1$, $\frac{3}{x^3}$, $\sqrt{x}$, and $6x^2 - y^3$ are *not* monomials.

Recall that the numerical factor of a term usually is called the coefficient. Thus, the following are the coefficients of the monomials given above.

$$-7 \qquad 15 \qquad 1 \qquad \frac{1}{2}$$

The **degree** of a monomial is the sum of the exponents of its variables. The degree of $\frac{1}{2}x^3y^2$ is 5. The degree of 15 is 0 since $15 = 15x^0$ $(x^0 = 1)$.

We have used the distributive property to simplify expressions by combining **like monomials** with only one variable. An example follows.

$$3x + 5x + 9 = 8x + 9$$

Like monomials are two monomials that are the same or differ only by their coefficients. An example of like monomials is $3abc^2$ and $-10abc^2$. You also can use the distributive property to simplify expressions containing like monomials with more than one variable.

Example   Simplify $-6xy + 8xy$.
$$-6xy + 8xy = (-6+8)xy \quad \textit{Use the distributive property.}$$
$$= 2xy$$

State whether each of the following expressions is a monomial. If it is, then name its coefficient.

1. -10
2. $14x + y$
3. $21xyz$
4. $-p^3q^2$
5. a^2
6. $\frac{2b}{5}$
7. $\sqrt{rs}$
8. $\frac{-x}{17}$
9. $\frac{4}{y}$
10. $\sqrt{11x}$

State the degree of each monomial.

11. $-by$
12. $7xy$
13. $6x^2y$
14. $\frac{-5}{7}p^2qr^4$
15. $39m$

Simplify each of the following if possible.

16. $-3xy + (-11xy)$
17. $-19y + 8y$
18. $5ab^2 + a^2b$
19. $16x^2 + 2x^2$
20. $3ab - 5ab$
21. $6x^3 + 3x^3 + 9x^3$
22. $2y^3 - 3y^3$
23. $8a^2 + a$
24. $4mn - mn$
25. $x^3 - \frac{1}{3}x^3 + \frac{5}{6}x^3$
26. $5ab - 7ab + 12ab$
27. $5y - \frac{y}{3} + 4y$

4.2 Subtracting Monomials

To subtract a signed number, you add its opposite. The opposite of a number is equal to the product of the number and -1.

The opposite of 8 is -8. $-1 \cdot 8 = -8$
The opposite of -5 is 5. $-1 \cdot -5 = 5$

To subtract monomials, they must be alike. Like monomials are the same or differ only by their coefficients.

To subtract one monomial from another, first multiply it by -1. Then add the new monomial.

Example 1   Find $15 - 7$.
$$15 - 7 = 15 + (-1)(7)$$
$$= 15 + (-7)$$
$$= 8$$

Example 2   Find $11x^2 - 6x^2$.
$$11x^2 - 6x^2 = 11x^2 + (-1)(6x^2)$$
$$= 11x^2 + (-6x^2)$$
$$= [11 + (-6)]x^2$$
$$= 5x^2$$

Example 3   Find $16x^2y^2 - 7x^2y^2$.
$$16x^2y^2 - 7x^2y^2 = 16x^2y^2 + (-1)(7x^2y^2)$$
$$= 16x^2y^2 + (-7x^2y^2)$$
$$= [16 + (-7)]x^2y^2$$
$$= 9x^2y^2$$

Subtraction problems can be checked by adding the answer to the subtrahend.

$$\text{Check:}\quad \begin{array}{ll} 9x^2y^2 & \text{difference} \\ + 7x^2y^2 & \text{subtrahend} \\ \hline 16x^2y^2 & \text{minuend} \end{array}$$

Find each of the following products.

1. $(-1)(-3x)$ 2. $(-1)(7ab)$ 3. $(-1)a$ 4. $(-1)4y^2$

5. $(-1)9$ 6. $(-1)(-10xy)$ 7. $(-1)(-5z)$ 8. $(-1)41x$

Find the difference. Check the answers by addition.

9. $66xy - 28xy$ 10. $75xyz - 17xyz$ 11. $353 - 272$ 12. $48y^2 - 27y^2$

13. $26a^2b - 25a^2b$ 14. $41x^2y^3 - (-16x^2y^3)$ 15. $7xy^2 - (-10xy^2)$

16. $51ab^2 - ab^2$ 17. $54abc - (-22abc)$ 18. $28c^2d^2 - (-21c^2d^2)$

19. $444 - (-69)$ 20. $14x^2y^3z - 13x^2y^3z$ 21. $45rst^2 - (-rst^2)$

22. $\frac{x}{2}y^2 - \frac{x}{4}y^2$ 23. $\frac{2}{3}cd^2 - \frac{(-cd^2)}{6}$ 24. $101a^3b^2c - (-11a^3b^2c)$

4.3 Multiplying Monomials

Since a monomial is itself a product, the product of two monomials is the product of these products.

$$3x^2 \cdot 2y^4 = (3 \cdot 2) \cdot x^2 \cdot y^4$$
$$= 6x^2 y^4$$

Now, suppose the factors contain powers of the *same base*. Recall that $x^2 = x \cdot x$.

$$x^2 \cdot x^4 = (x \cdot x) \quad \cdot \quad (x \cdot x \cdot x \cdot x) \text{ or } \qquad x^6$$
$$\text{2 factors} \quad + \quad \text{4 factors} \quad \text{are } \text{6 factors.}$$

From many such examples, you can conclude that you add the exponents when you find the product of powers to the same base.

> **For all numbers a and positive integers m and n,**
> $$a^m \cdot a^n = a^{m+n}.$$

Example 1 Find the product $(2x)(5x^3)$.

$$(2x)(5x^3) = (2 \cdot 5)(x \cdot x^3)$$
$$= 10x^{1+3} \qquad \qquad \textit{Recall } x = x^1.$$
$$= 10x^4$$

The following is an example of a power of a power.

$$(x^2)^3 = x^2 \cdot x^2 \cdot x^2$$
$$= x^{2+2+2} \qquad \textit{Use the rule for the product of powers.}$$
$$= x^6 \qquad \qquad \textit{How do you obtain the exponent 6 from}$$
$$\qquad \qquad \qquad \textit{the exponents 2 and 3?}$$

Six is the product of 2 and 3. Try several other examples. You can conclude the following rule for the power of a power.

> **For all numbers a and positive integers m and n,**
> $$(a^m)^n = a^{mn}.$$

Example 2 Simplify $(r^4)^2$.

$$(r^4)^2 = r^{4 \cdot 2} \quad \textit{Use the rule for the power of a power.}$$
$$= r^8$$

Another situation is the power of a product. Study the following example.

$$(xy)^3 = (xy)(xy)(xy)$$
$$= x^3 y^3$$

For this and other similar examples, you can conclude the following.

> **For all numbers a and b and positive integer m,**
> $$(ab)^m = a^m b^m.$$

Example 3 Simplify $(3xy)^3$.
$$(3xy)^3 = 3^3 \cdot x^3 \cdot y^3$$
$$= 27x^3y^3$$

Example 4 Simplify $(4a^2b^3)^3$.
$$(4a^2b^3)^3 = 4^3 \cdot (a^2)^3 \cdot (b^3)^3$$
$$= 64 \cdot a^{2 \cdot 3} \cdot b^{3 \cdot 3}$$
$$= 64a^6b^9$$

In example 4 you use the rules for the power of a power and the power of a product. The rule for the power of a monomial can be stated as follows.

For all numbers *a* and *b* and positive integers *m*, *n*, and *p*,
$$(a^m b^n)^p = a^{mp} b^{np}.$$

Example 5 Simplify $(-2x^3y^2)^4$.
$$(-2x^3y^2)^4 = (-2)^4 \cdot (x^3)^4 \cdot (y^2)^4$$
$$= 16 \cdot x^{3 \cdot 4} \cdot y^{2 \cdot 4}$$
$$= 16x^{12}y^8$$

Verify each of the following by multiplication.

Sample: Verify $2^2 \cdot 2^3 = 2^5$.
$$2^2 \cdot 2^3 \stackrel{?}{=} 2^5$$
$$4 \cdot 8 \stackrel{?}{=} 32$$
$$32 = 32$$

1. $5^3 \cdot 5^2 = 5^5$ 　　2. $3^2 \cdot 3 = 3^3$ 　3. $2^1 \cdot 2^2 = 2^3$ 　　4. $6^2 \cdot 6^2 = 6^4$

5. $2^2 \cdot 2^5 = 2^7$ 　　6. $(2^2)^3 = 2^6$ 　7. $(2^2)^2 = 2^4$ 　　8. $(-2)^3(-2)^4 = (-2)^7$

9. $(12 \cdot 2^3)^2 = 12^2 \cdot 2^6$ 　10. $(2^2)^5 = 2^{10}$ 　11. $(3 \cdot 2^2)^4 = 3^4 2^8$ 　12. $(2 \cdot 3)^2 = 2^2 \cdot 3^2$

Find each of the following products.

13. $(2ab)(-2c)$ 　　14. $(-4x)(2x^2)$ 　　15. $c^2 \cdot c^2$ 　　16. $y^4 \cdot y^7$

17. $(3x)(6y^2)$ 　　18. $x^2 \cdot x^5$ 　　19. $y^3 \cdot y^3$ 　　20. $x^6 \cdot x \cdot x^3$

21. $d \cdot d^4$ 　　22. $(8a^2b^3)(3b^4)$ 　　23. $(x^2y^2)(xy^3)$ 　　24. $(xy)(10x^2)$

25. $(7c^2d^3)(-4c^5d^6)$ 26. $(7x^2y^4)(12x^6y^8)$ 27. $(8c^2d^4)(-5c^6d^2)$

28. $(9c^9d^8)(12c^5d^2)$ 　　29. $(8c^5d^7)(13c^2d^8)$ 　　30. $(6w^3z^4)(-3w^2z^5)(8w^9z^8)$

31. $(3w^2v)(-2w^5v^2)(4w^6v^5)$ 32. $(-2w^2v^7)(-4w^3v^2)$ 　33. $(8x^3y^2z^6)(-9x^9y^6z^5)$

Simplify.

34. $(m^3)^2$ 　　35. $(n^3)^9$ 　　36. $(a^2)^3$ 　　37. $(4a)^2$

38. $(x^3)^4$ 　　39. $(-2y)^5$ 　　40. $(-4x^6y^4z^8)^3$ 　　41. $(xy)^7$

42. $(3a^2)^6$ 　　43. $(x^3y^5)^2$ 　　44. $(-6x^5y^3z^9)^3$ 　　45. $(-3x^3y^2z^5)^4$

38

4.4 Dividing Monomials

You found that exponents are added when you multiply powers of the same base. You would expect that exponents are subtracted when you divide powers. Indeed, this is the case.

Example 1   Simplify $\dfrac{x^5}{x^3}$.

$$\frac{x^5}{x^3} = \frac{x \cdot x \cdot x \cdot x \cdot x}{x \cdot x \cdot x} \qquad \begin{array}{l} 5 \text{ factors} \\ 3 \text{ factors} \end{array}$$
$$= x \cdot x \qquad\qquad 2 \text{ or } (5-3) \text{ factors}$$
$$= x^2$$

The following example illustrates that another definition is needed for some exponents.

Example 2   Simplify $\dfrac{x^2}{x^6}$.

$$\frac{x^2}{x^6} = \frac{x \cdot x}{x \cdot x \cdot x \cdot x \cdot x \cdot x}$$
$$= \frac{1}{x^4}$$

Suppose in example 2 you subtract exponents. Then, $\dfrac{x^2}{x^6} = x^{2-6}$ or x^{-4}. What is the meaning of a negative exponent? We define a negative exponent as follows.

> **For every nonzero number a and every positive integer n, $a^{-n} = \dfrac{1}{a^n}$.**

Example 3   Simplify $\dfrac{x^3}{x^3}$.

$$\frac{x^3}{x^3} = \frac{x \cdot x \cdot x}{x \cdot x \cdot x}$$
$$= 1$$

By subtracting exponents in example 3 produces the result $x^{3-3} = x^0$.
Because of example 3 and others like it, we define a zero exponent as follows.

> **For every nonzero number a, $a^0 = 1$.**

From many examples you can conclude the following rule for dividing powers. The definitions of negative and zero exponents permit the rule to be applied generally.

> **For every nonzero number a and every positive integer m and n, $\dfrac{a^m}{a^n} = a^{m-n}$.**

If m is greater than n, as in example 1, use the rule as it is given. If n is greater than m, as in example 2, $m - n$ is negative. In such a case it may be simpler to use the rule in the following form.

$$\frac{a^m}{a^n} = \frac{1}{a^{n-m}}$$

In example 2, $\frac{x^2}{x^6} = \frac{1}{x^{6-2}}$ or $\frac{1}{x^4}$. Notice that $-(n - m) = m - n$.

Example 4 Simplify $\frac{49a^4b^7c^2}{7ab^4c^3}$.

$$\frac{49a^4b^7c^2}{7ab^4c^3} = \left(\frac{49}{7}\right)\left(\frac{a^4}{a}\right)\left(\frac{b^7}{b^4}\right)\left(\frac{c^2}{c^3}\right) \quad \text{Notice that } \frac{xy}{zw} = \left(\frac{x}{z}\right)\left(\frac{y}{w}\right).$$

$$= 7 \cdot a^{4-1} \cdot b^{7-4} \cdot c^{2-3}$$

$$= 7a^3b^3c^{-1} \text{ or } \frac{7a^3b^3}{c}$$

You may have noticed that the rule for dividing powers is really an extension of the rule for multiplying powers. Suppose a is any number and m and n are positive integers. Study the following.

$$\frac{a^m}{a^n} = a^m \cdot \frac{1}{a^n} \quad \text{State the quotient as a product.}$$

$$= a^m \cdot a^{-n} \quad \text{Use the definition of a negative exponent.}$$

$$= a^{m+(-n)} \quad \text{Use the rule for the product of powers.}$$

$$= a^{m-n}$$

Verify each of the following by multiplication and division.

1. $\dfrac{2^6}{2^4} = 2^2$

2. $\dfrac{4^5}{4^2} = 4^3$

3. $\dfrac{3^3}{3^2} = 3^1$

4. $\dfrac{6^3}{6^4} = \dfrac{1}{6}$

5. $\dfrac{7^2}{7^2} = 7^0$

6. $\dfrac{8^2}{8^0} = 8^2$

7. $\dfrac{5^1}{5^3} = 5^{-2}$

8. $\dfrac{2^5 \cdot 5^3}{2^3 \cdot 5^4} = \dfrac{2^2}{5^1}$

Simplify each of the following.

9. $\dfrac{y^7}{y^6}$

10. $\dfrac{a^6}{a^2}$

11. $\dfrac{b^3}{b^7}$

12. $\dfrac{x^4}{x^9}$

13. $\dfrac{an^5}{n^2}$

14. $\dfrac{xy^7}{xy^4}$

15. $\dfrac{x^4t^9}{-xt^6}$

16. $\dfrac{-a^2b^4}{a^4b^8}$

17. $\dfrac{21rst^3}{3r^2t}$

18. $\dfrac{18b^4}{6b^2}$

19. $\dfrac{81m^5n^4}{9m^3n^9}$

20. $\dfrac{36b^4c^2}{4bc^5}$

21. $\dfrac{108c^4d^9}{9c^{12}d^3}$

22. $\dfrac{10m^4}{40m}$

23. $\dfrac{72m^5n^2}{8m^3n^7}$

24. $\dfrac{6r^4s^8}{-30r^3s^2}$

25. $\dfrac{3x^4y^7}{12x^9y^2}$

26. $\dfrac{12x^{15}y^8}{8x^5y^{10}}$

27. $\dfrac{48c^5d^4}{40c^2d^5}$

28. $\dfrac{-6x^5y^3}{42x^2y^8}$

29. $\dfrac{16a^{-3}b^2c^{-1}}{48a^{-3}b^7c^2}$

30. $\dfrac{11abc^{-2}}{33a^2b^2}$

31. $\dfrac{12c^3d^{-4}f^7}{60c^{-2}d^{-6}f^4}$

32. $\dfrac{3x^{-3}z^2}{12x^{-2}y^2z^2}$

33. $\dfrac{-35r^5s^8}{5r^5s^2}$

34. $\dfrac{90n^5m^9}{90nm^7}$

35. $\dfrac{a^2b^5}{-8a^3b^6}$

36. $\dfrac{-10a^5b^9}{-50a^2b^8}$

37. $\dfrac{-6x^2y^3z^9}{24x^2y^7z^9}$

38. $\dfrac{ab^5c^8}{8ab^6c^9}$

39. $\dfrac{4x}{11xyz^7}$

40. $\dfrac{8a^3b^6c}{48a^3b^7c^4}$

41. $\dfrac{14bc}{14b^3c}$

42. $\dfrac{-2a^3b^6}{24a^2b^2}$

43. $\dfrac{5xy^2z^5}{25x^5y^3z}$

44. $\dfrac{12c^3d^{14}f^6}{60cd^6f^3}$

45. $\dfrac{48a^3b^6c}{48a^3b^7c^4}$

46. $\dfrac{-11abc^2}{44a^2b^5c^7}$

47. $\dfrac{-9c^4d^5}{-45c^3d^3}$

48. $\dfrac{4a^2bc}{16ab}$

4.5 Scientific Notation

Persons in technical fields often work with very large or very small quantities. For example, the distance from the sun to the planet Neptune is about 2,790,000,000 miles and the weight of one molecule of water is 0.00000000000000000000003 gram. It is simpler to compute with these numbers when they are expressed in **scientific notation**.

A number is expressed in scientific notation when it is in the following form.

$$a \times 10^n \qquad \text{where } a \text{ is between 1 and 10 and } n \text{ is an integer.}$$

Example 1 Express 2,790,000,000 and 0.00000000000000000000003 in scientific notation.

$$2{,}790{,}000{,}000 = 2.79 \times 10^9$$

9 places

$$0.00000000000000000000003 = 3.0 \times 10^{-23}$$

23 places

Numbers expressed in scientific notation can be multiplied using the rule for the product of powers.

Example 2 Find $(2 \times 10^{-5})(4 \times 10^9)$.

$$(2 \times 10^{-5})(4 \times 10^9) = (2)(4)(10^{-5})(10^9)$$
$$= 8 \times 10^{-5+9} \qquad \textit{Use the rule for the product of powers.}$$
$$= 8 \times 10^4$$

Express each of the following in scientific notation.

1. 6800
2. 530,000
3. 0.0095
4. 0.00000025
5. 70,000
6. 88,000,000,000
7. 100,000,000
8. 0.00096
9. 0.003
10. 0.00077
11. 23,000,000
12. 0.000000000000156

Express each product in scientific notation.

13. $(2 \times 10^4)(3 \times 10^6)$
14. $(3.5 \times 10^{-7})(3.5 \times 10^{16})$
15. $(4.3 \times 10^3)(3.0 \times 10^{-5})$
16. $(4 \times 10^4)(2 \times 10^8)$
17. $(3 \times 10^{-4})(5 \times 10^{-8})$
18. $(8.1 \times 10^{-3})(6.7 \times 10^{-2})$
19. $(4.4 \times 10^{-4})(5.6 \times 10^{10})$
20. $(4.5 \times 10^5)(7.2 \times 10^3)$
21. $(2.3 \times 10^{-8})(1.4 \times 10^4)$
22. $(4.7 \times 10^{-4})(4.1 \times 10^{-4})$
23. $(5.2 \times 10^4)(3.2 \times 10^2)$
24. $(3.3 \times 10^{-3})(4.1 \times 10^3)$
25. $(9 \times 10^{-4})(5 \times 10^{-3})(6 \times 10^{-3})$
26. $(2 \times 10^4)(5 \times 10^6)(3 \times 10^4)$
27. $(2 \times 10^4)(2 \times 10^{-3})(4 \times 10^{-8})$
28. $(8 \times 10^4)(0.0002)(4 \times 10^{-4})$
29. $(4 \times 10^{-6})(3 \times 10^2)(15 \times 10^4)$
30. $(5000)(0.0005)(6 \times 10^4)$
31. $(8{,}000{,}000)(0.0035)(0.00003)$
32. $(3000)(2 \times 10^4)(7 \times 10^2)$

4.6 Adding and Subtracting Polynomials

Expressions such as $5x+1$, x^2y+x, and $5-3y+6y^2$ are called **polynomials**. Notice that each is the sum or difference of two or more monomials. The expression $x^2+\frac{9}{x}$ is not a polynomial because $\frac{9}{x}$ is not a monomial.

The following table lists some special polynomials and an example of each.

Polynomial	Number of Terms	Example
Monomial	1	$14ax^2$
Binomial	2	x^2y+x
Trinomial	3	$5-3y+6y^2$

The **degree of a polynomial** is the degree of the monomial of greatest degree.
The **degree of a monomial** is the sum of the exponents of its variables.
The polynomial containing one variable is in **standard form** if the powers of the variable are arranged in descending order. The polynomial $x^4+3x^3-5x^2+x-1$ has degree 4 and is in standard form.
You can use the distributive property to add polynomials.

Example 1 Find the sum of $3xy^2+2x^2y$ and $6xy^2-x^2y$.

$$(3xy^2+2x^2y)+(6xy^2-x^2y) = (3xy^2+6xy^2)+(2xy^2-x^2y)$$
$$= (3+6)xy^2+(2-1)x^2y$$
$$= 9xy^2+x^2y$$

Example 2 Find the sum of $14x^2+10x+14$ and $21x-67x^2$.
Sometimes its helpful to write the polynomials in standard form and arrange like monomials in vertical columns.

$$\begin{array}{r} 14x^2+10x+14 \\ -67x^2+21x \quad\ \\ \hline -53x^2+31x+14 \end{array}$$

State the degree of each of the following polynomials.

1. $9x^2+2x^5+8x-3$ **2.** $6x^5+5-4x^4+4x^2+3x^3$ **3.** $3x^4+6x+8x^2-1$

4. $6x^3y^5-9x^2y^2+2x^5y^2$ **5.** $5xyz^2+5x^2y^2z+5z^5$ **6.** $2x^2y^3-8x^4y^3+17xy^2$

Write each polynomial in standard form.

7. $11x^2-6x^3+9x-1$ **8.** $28x-5x^3+3x^2-2$ **9.** $18x^3-2x+3x^2-7$

Find each sum.

10. $(19n-7m)+(10n-3m)$ **11.** $(5x^2-5x+2)+(-3x^2-4x-1)$

12. $(9x-2y)+(4x+4y)$ **13.** $(6m^2+m-9)+(-6m^2+6m+9)$

14. $(9w^2+3w-8)+(6w^2-5w+5)$

43

15.
$$5a^2 - 6a + 5$$
$$\underline{9a^2 + 3a - 9}$$

16.
$$13c^2 + 4c - 9$$
$$\underline{3c^2 - 9c + 8}$$

17. $(y^2 - 3y + 6) + (-2y - 6 + 8y^2)$

18. $(21xy - 8x^2 - 9y^2) + (7x^2 + 14xy)$

19. $(21x^2y + 2y^3 + 11) + (-6x^2y - 4xy^2 + 5y^3)$

20. $(8x + 3x^2 - 6) + (5 - 11x + x^2)$

In an earlier section monomials were subtracted. Polynomials are handled in the same way. To subtract one polynomial from another, first multiply it by –1. Then add the new polynomial. Study the following example.

Example 1 Find $(3x - 5y) - (6x - 8y)$.
$$
\begin{aligned}
(3x - 5y) - (6x - 8y) &= (3x - 5y) + (-1)(6x - 8y) \\
&= (3x - 5y) + (-6x + 8y) \\
&= [3x + (-6x)] + [(-5y) + 8y) \quad \textit{Combine like terms.} \\
&= -3x + 3y
\end{aligned}
$$

You can check subtraction problems by adding the answer to the subtrahend.

Example 2 Find $(-6b^2 + 13b) - (5 + b - 2b^2)$ and check by addition.

$$-6b^2 + 13b$$
$$\underline{-2b^2 + b + 5}$$
$\xrightarrow{\quad -1(-2b^2 + b + 5) \quad}$
$$-6b^2 + 13b$$
$$\underline{2b^2 - b - 5}$$
$$-4b^2 + 12b - 5$$

Check:
$$-4b^2 + 12b - 5 \quad \textit{difference}$$
$$\underline{-2b^2 + b + 5} \quad \textit{subtrahend}$$
$$-6b^2 + 13b \quad \textit{minuend}$$

Find each of the following products.

21. $(-1)(-5x)$

22. $(-1)a$

23. $(-1)(4x + 2y)$

24. $(-1)(4ab)$

25. $(-1)(a - b)$

26. $(-1)(x^3 - x - 1)$

27. $(-1)(-9m^2 + 3m + 1)$

28. $(-1)(-8x + 11)$

29. $(-1)(2a^2 + 3b - 1)$

Find each difference. Check your answers by addition.

30. $(6x - y) - (7x + 3y)$

31. $(9w^2 + 5w - 8) - (6w^2 + 8w - 9)$

32. $(2a + 10b) - (a - 4b)$

33. $(5x^2 + 6x - 9) - (3x^2 - 4x + 8)$

34. $(6x^2 + 4x - 5) - (9x^2 - 3x + 2)$

35. $(5a^2 - 4a + 2) - (3a^2 - 2a + 9)$

36. $(2b^2 + b - 18) - (6 - 3b^2 + 4b)$

37.
$$y^2 + x^2$$
$$\underline{-(-4y^2 + 8xy - x^2)}$$

38.
$$15c^2 + 6c - 8$$
$$\underline{-(8c^2 - 5c + 3)}$$

39. $(c^2 + 2c - 16) - [(-8c^2) - 11c + 16]$

40. $(x^2y^2 - xy + 10) - (-18 - 4xy)$

4.7 Multiplying Polynomials

You can use the distributive property to multiply a polynomial by a monomial.

Example 1 Find the product of $3x$ and $4y + 7xy + 2$.

$$3x(4y + 7xy + 2) = 3x(4y) + 3x(7xy) + 3x(2)$$
$$= 12xy + 21x^2y + 6x$$

You can also use the distributive property to multiply polynomials.

Example 2 Find $(x + 7)(x + 4)$.

Multiply each term of the first polynomial times the second polynomial.

$$(x + 7)(x + 4) = x(x + 4) + 7(x + 4)$$
$$= x(x) + x(4) + 7(x) + 7(4)$$
$$= x^2 + 4x + 7x + 28$$
$$= x^2 + 11x + 28$$

A shortcut for multiplying binomials is shown in example 3.

Example 3 Find the product $(x + 7)(x + 4)$ using the shortcut.

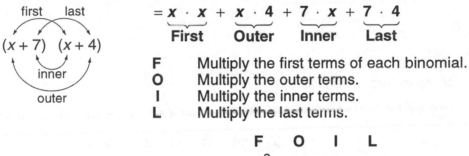

$$= x \cdot x + x \cdot 4 + 7 \cdot x + 7 \cdot 4$$

First   Outer   Inner   Last

F   Multiply the first terms of each binomial.
O   Multiply the outer terms.
I   Multiply the inner terms.
L   Multiply the last terms.

$$\begin{array}{cccc} \textbf{F} & \textbf{O} & \textbf{I} & \textbf{L} \end{array}$$
$$= x^2 + 4x + 7x + 28$$

$$\begin{array}{ccc} \textbf{F} & \textbf{O and I} & \textbf{L} \end{array}$$
$$= x^2 + (4 + 7)x + 28 \qquad \textit{Combine like terms.}$$
$$= x^2 + 11x + 28$$

This process is called **FOIL** (**F**irst, **O**uter, **I**nner, **L**ast) method for multiplying binomials. With practice you will begin combining like terms as you multiply.

Example 4 Find $(3x + 5)(x - 2)$ using the FOIL method.

$$\begin{array}{cccc} \textbf{F} & \textbf{O} & \textbf{I} & \textbf{L} \end{array}$$
$$(3x + 5)(x - 2) = 3x \cdot x + 3x(-2) + 5 \cdot x + 5(-2)$$
$$= 3x^2 + [(-6) + 5]x - 10$$
$$= 3x^2 - x - 10$$

Example 5 Find $(2x-6)(x^2+3x-7)$.

$$\begin{aligned}
(2x-6)(x^2+3x-7) &= 2x(x^2+3x-7)+(-6)(x^2+3x-7)\\
&= 2x(x^2)+2x(3x)+2x(-7)+(-6)(x^2)+(-6)(3x)+(-6)(-7)\\
&= 2x^3+6x^2-14x-6x^2-18x+42\\
&= 2x^3-32x+42
\end{aligned}$$

Find each of the following products.

1. $3a(a^2+b)$

2. $x^2(x-4)$

3. $3r(s-r)$

4. $4x^2(3x-2xy)$

5. $-3x(3x-5y)$

6. $(5-x)5x$

7. $8n(2n^2+5n+5)$

8. $6m(10m^2-7m+6)$

9. $5n^2(3n^2-5n+1)$

10. $4a(7y^2-7ay+5a^2)$

11. $2a^2b(b^3+4ab^2+a^2)$

12. $(3x^2y)(5x^3y-5xy+2x^2y^2)$

Complete each of the following.

13. $(x+6)(x+5) = \underline{\hspace{1cm}}(x+5) + \underline{\hspace{1cm}}(x+5)$

14. $(3y+2)(y+2) = \underline{\hspace{1cm}}(y+2) + \underline{\hspace{1cm}}(y+2)$

15. $(x+7)(3x-4) = x(\underline{\hspace{1cm}}) + 7(\underline{\hspace{1cm}})$

16. $(5a-8)(5a-3) = 5a(\underline{\hspace{1cm}}) - 8(\underline{\hspace{1cm}})$

State the product indicated in each exercise.

17. Inner terms $(x+6)(x+9)$

18. Outer terms, $(x+7)(x-6)$

19. Last terms, $(x+5)(x+7)$

20. First terms, $(x+2)(x-21)$

21. Outer terms, $(a-2)(a+1)$

22. Last terms, $(11+y)(7-y)$

Find each product.

23. $(a-3)(a+5)$

24. $(x+3)(x-3)$

25. $(2x-5)(3x+4)$

26. $(y+2)(y+7)$

27. $(3x-6)(2x+5)$

28. $(3x+5)(2x-6)$

29. $(4x+9)(3x-5)$

30. $(6x+1)(4x-7)$

31. $(4x+5)(4x-5)$

32. $(2x-3)(4x+7)$

33. $(7x-3)(8x-5)$

34. $(5m+6n)^2$

35. $(3x+5)(2x-7)$

36. $(c+5)^2$

37. $(3x-6)^2$

38. $(x+2)(x^2+3x+4)$

39. $(x-1)(x^4+x^3+x^2+1)$

40. $(x+3)(x^2+2x+1)$

41. $(2x+1)(x^2+x+1)$

42. $(-2xy+3y^2)(x-6xy-5y^2)$

43. $(3x+2y)(9x^2+12xy+4y^2)$

44. $(3x^2-16x)(3x^2-2x)$

4.8 Dividing Polynomials by Monomials

To divide a polynomial by a monomial, divide each term of the polynomial by the monomial.

Example 1 Divide $6x^3 + 12x^2 - 9x + 18$ by $3x$.

$$\frac{6x^3 + 12x^2 - 9x + 18}{3x} = \frac{6x^3}{3x} + \frac{12x^2}{3x} - \frac{9x}{3x} + \frac{18}{3x}$$
$$= 2x^2 + 4x - 3 + \frac{6}{x}$$

Example 2 Divide $5x^3y - 20x^2y^2 + 15xy^5$ by $5x^2y$.

$$\frac{5x^3y - 20x^2y^2 + 15xy^5}{5x^2y} = \frac{5x^3y}{5x^2y} - \frac{20x^2y^2}{5x^2y} + \frac{15xy^5}{5x^2y}$$
$$= x - 4y + \frac{3y^4}{x}$$

Find each quotient.

1. $\dfrac{4^5}{4^4}$

2. $\dfrac{y^8}{y^2}$

3. $\dfrac{6y^2 + 4}{2}$

4. $\dfrac{11b^3 + b}{b}$

5. $\dfrac{15x^8}{5x^5}$

6. $\dfrac{44a^7}{11a}$

7. $\dfrac{5b^2c^2 - 40bc}{20}$

8. $\dfrac{12c^2 - 4c}{4c}$

9. $\dfrac{9r^2s^2 + 3rs - 12r^2s}{3rs}$

10. $\dfrac{7pq^2 - 5pq + 2p^2q}{pq}$

11. $\dfrac{49x^5 + 63x^3 - 84x^2}{-7x^2}$

12. $\dfrac{a^4b^2 - a^2b + 2a}{ab}$

13. $\dfrac{10x^2y^4 - 14x^2y^5 + 6xy}{2xy}$

14. $\dfrac{a^3b^2 - a^2b + 4ab}{ab}$

15. $\dfrac{24c^2d^3f - 12d^5f^2 + 36cd}{18cdf}$

16. $\dfrac{12x^3y^5 + 18x^3y + 36xy^3}{6xy}$

17. $\dfrac{25a^7b^5c^3 + 15a^5bc - 5a}{20ab}$

18. $\dfrac{3xyz^2 - 24xy^2z^3 + 36x^2yz}{18x^2yz}$

19. $\dfrac{3 + 24st - 6rs^2t^2}{3rs^2t}$

20. $\dfrac{15a^2b^2 - 6a^4b^4c + 18ab^2c^9}{3ab^2}$

21. $\dfrac{14r^2s^2 - 14rs - rst^5}{2rs}$

22. $\dfrac{6xyz^3 + 12xy - 2x^2y^2z^2}{2xz^2}$

23. $\dfrac{6abc + 18b^2c - 3a^2b^3d}{6a^2b^2c}$

24. $\dfrac{15xyz + 25yz^2 + 10z}{5xz}$

25. $\dfrac{3abc + 60a^2bc^3 + 18ac^4}{6a^2b^2c^2}$

26. $\dfrac{16x^2y + 24xyz^2 + 32x^2y^4z^2}{4x}$

47

4.9 Dividing Polynomials by Polynomials

To divide a polynomial with more than one term, you can use a procedure similar to long division. Compare examples 1 and 2.

Example 1 Divide 672 by 16.

Step 1   Divide 67 by 16.
The quotient is 4 + a remainder.
Multiply 16 by 4. Put the product of
64 under the 67.
Subtract 64 from 67.
The difference is 3.
Bring down the 2.

Step 2   Divide 32 by 16. The quotient is 2.
Multiply 16 by 2. The product is 32.
Subtract 32 from 32. The reminder is 0.
Thus, $672 \div 16 = 42$.

$$
\begin{array}{r}
42 \\
16\overline{)672} \\
64 \\
\hline
32 \\
32 \\
\hline
0
\end{array}
$$

Example 2   Divide $7x + x^2 + 12$ by $4 + x$.
Write both polynomials in standard form.
$$x^2 + 7x + 12 \text{ and } x + 4.$$

Divide x^2 by x. The quotient is x.
Multiply $x + 4$ by x.

Subtract $x^2 + 4x$ from $x^2 + 7x$.
Bring down the 12.
Divide $3x$ by x. The quotient is 3.
Multiply $x + 4$ by 3.
Subtract $3x + 12$ from $3x + 12$.
The remainder is 0.

$$
\begin{array}{r}
x + 3 \\
x + 4\overline{)x^2 + 7x + 12} \\
x^2 + 4x \\
\hline
3x + 12 \\
3x + 12 \\
\hline
0
\end{array}
$$

In this type of problem, stop dividing when the remainder is 0 or its degree is less than the degree of the divisor.

Thus, $(x^2 + 7x + 12) \div (x + 4) = x + 3$.

Since only like terms can be subtracted in each step, it sometimes is necessary to insert a term with 0 as its coefficient. Study this method in example 3.

Example 3   Find $\dfrac{y^2 + 9}{y - 3}$.

$$
\begin{array}{r}
y + 3 \\
y - 3\overline{)y^2 + 0 \cdot y + 9} \\
y^2 - 3y \\
\hline
3y + 9 \\
3y - 9 \\
\hline
18
\end{array}
$$

Insert $0 \cdot y$ as a placeholder.

Why is this permissible?

The degree of 18 is 0.
Therefore you stop dividing because the degree of 18 is less than the degree of $(y - 3)$ or 1.
The remainder is 18.

Thus $\frac{y^2+9}{y-3} = y+3$ with remainder 18. This answer also can be written

$$\frac{y^2+9}{y-3} = y+3+\frac{18}{y-3}.$$

Solve the following problems.

1. $\dfrac{2x^2+3x-2}{2x-1}$

2. $\dfrac{x^3+2x^2-5x+12}{x+4}$

3. $\dfrac{y^2+3y+2}{y+2}$

4. $\dfrac{8m^3+27}{2m+3}$

5. $\dfrac{b^2+8b-20}{b+10}$

6. $\dfrac{t^3-19t+9}{t-4}$

7. $\dfrac{3s^2+8s+4}{3s+2}$

8. $\dfrac{9d^3+5d-8}{3d-2}$

9. $\dfrac{y^4-81}{y-3}$

10. $\dfrac{2x^3-5x^2+22x+51}{2x+3}$

11. $\dfrac{x^2-16}{x-4}$

12. $\dfrac{9y^2-49}{3y-7}$

13. Divide $15t^2-29t-14$ by $3t-7$.

14. Divide $2m^2+13m-18$ by $2m+3$.

15. Divide $6x^2+31x+28$ by $6x+7$.

16. Divide $x^4+x^3+7x^2-x-8$ by $x-1$,

17. Divide $14y^2-17y-9$ by $2y+3$.

18. Divide $x^4-x^3-9x^2+14x-4$ by x^2-3x+1.

19. Divide x^4-1 by $x+1$.

20. Divide x^8-256 by $x-2$.

21. Divide $x^4+2x^3+3x^2+5x-2$ by $x+2$.

4.10 Factoring Integers

A number is said to be **factored** if it is expressed as the product of two or more numbers. You can find factors of a number by division. Factor 20 into positive integers.

$20 \div 1 = 20$	$20 \div 2 = 10$	$20 \div 4 = 5$	The factors of 20 are
$20 \div 20 = 1$	$20 \div 10 = 2$	$20 \div 5 = 4$	20, 10, 5, 4, 2, and 1.

Continue the factoring process.

$20 = 2 \cdot 10$ $20 = 4 \cdot 5$ No positive integers divide evenly into the numbers 2 and 5 besides the numbers themselves.

$2 \cdot 2 \cdot 5$ $2 \cdot 2 \cdot 5$

The numbers 2 and 5 are called **prime numbers**.

> **A prime number is an integer, greater than 1, whose only positive factors are 1 and itself.**

The prime factorization of a number is the product of the prime factors of the number.

For example, the prime factorization of 20 is $2 \cdot 2 \cdot 5$ or $2^2 \cdot 5$.
Consider the prime factorizations of 30 and 45.

$$30 = 2 \cdot \mathbf{3} \cdot \mathbf{5} \qquad 45 = 3 \cdot \mathbf{3} \cdot \mathbf{5}$$

The integers 30 and 45 have common factors 3 and 5, shown above in heavy black type. The product of these, 15, is called the **greatest common factor** (GCF) of 30 and 45.

Example 1   Find the GCF of 12 and 18.
The prime factorization of 12 is $\mathbf{2} \cdot 2 \cdot \mathbf{3}$.
The prime factorization of 18 is $\mathbf{2} \cdot \mathbf{3} \cdot 3$.
The common factors are 2 and 3.
The GCF is $2 \cdot 3$ or 6.

Example 2   Find the GCF of 72 and 126.
The prime factorization of 72 is $2 \cdot 2 \cdot \mathbf{2} \cdot \mathbf{3} \cdot \mathbf{3}$.
The prime factorization of 126 is $\mathbf{2} \cdot \mathbf{3} \cdot \mathbf{3} \cdot 7$.

The common factors are 2 and 3^2.

The GCF is $2 \cdot 3^2$ of 18.

Match each expression on the left with the corresponding group of numbers.

1. Prime factors of 24	**a.**	6
2. Greatest common factor of 24 and 42	**b.**	2,3
3. Factors of 24	**c.**	$2 \cdot 2 \cdot 2 \cdot 3$
4. Prime factorization of 24	**d.**	2, 3, 5, 7
5. Prime numbers in {1, 2, 3, 4, 5, 6, 7, 8}	**e.**	1, 2, 3
	f.	1, 2, 3, 4, 6, 8, 12, 24

Find the prime factorization of each of the following. Write each negative integer as the product of -1 and its prime factor.

6. 40

7. 68

8. 21

9. 60

10. -12

11. 80

12. -26

13. 304

14. -96

15. -112

16. 5005

17. 75

18. 81

Find the GCF for each pair of integers.

19. 15, 24

20. 4, 12

21. -9, 30

22. 12,18

23. -11, 33

24. 252,126

25. 216, 384

26. 20, 44

27. 27,36

28. 8, 20

29. 13, 39

30. 5, 50

31. 95, 304

32. 28, 54, 72

33. 12, 18, 30

34. 24, 28, 36

35. 24, 44

36. 18, 6, 42

37. 21, 14, 35

38. 60, 70

39. 72, 28

40. 56, 49

41. 42, 54, 66

42. -90, -38, 72

43. 14, 18, 2

44. -48, 16, 72

45. 12, 1, 36

46. 96, 30, 66

47. 15, 30, 20

48. 128, 112

49. -10, 16

4.11 Factoring Polynomials

The greatest common factor of two or more monomials is the common factor with the greatest numerical factor and the greatest degree.

Example 1 Find the GCF of $60x^3y^5$ and $90x^5y^2$.

$$60x^3y^5 = 2 \cdot 2 \cdot 3 \cdot 5 \cdot x \cdot x \cdot x \cdot y \cdot y \cdot y \cdot y \cdot y$$
$$90x^5y^2 = 2 \cdot 3 \cdot 3 \cdot 5x \cdot x \cdot x \cdot x \cdot x \cdot y \cdot y$$

The GCF of $60x^3y^5$ and $90x^5y^2$ is $2 \cdot 3 \cdot 5 \cdot x \cdot x \cdot x \cdot y \cdot y$ or $30x^3y^2$.

A polynomial has the GCF of its terms as a factor. Recall that you can find factors of a product by division. Another factor is the quotient of the polynomial and the GCF of its terms.

Example 2 Factor $4x^2 - 3x$.

$$4x^2 = 2 \cdot 2 \cdot x \cdot x \qquad \textit{Find the GCF of the terms of } 4x^2 - 3x.$$
$$-3x = -1 \cdot 3 \cdot x \qquad \textit{The GCF is x.}$$
$$(4x^2 - 3x) \div x = 4x - 3 \qquad \textit{Divide the polynomial by the GCF.}$$

The factored form of $4x^2 - 3x$ is $x(4x - 3)$.

Notice that $4x^2 - 3x = x(4x - 3)$ is an example of the distributive property.

Find the greatest common factor of each of the following pairs of monomials.

1. $22y^2$ and $33y^3$
2. $-25ab$ and 35
3. $10x^2$ and $35x$
4. $6rst$ and $54r^2s^3t^2$
5. $18m^2n^3$ and $15m^5n^6$
6. $27a^2b^3$ and $27a^4b$
7. $12xy$ and $14z^3$
8. $60x^2$ and $68a^2$
9. $105x^2y^2$ and $66xy^2$

Find the greatest common factor of the terms of each polynomial.

10. $14ab + 28b$
11. $3x^2y + 12xyz^2$
12. $9y^2 - 27y + 36$
13. $14abc^2 + 18c$
14. $2xy^3 + 4x^2y - 9x^3y^2$
15. $7y^2 - 21y$
16. $4x^2y^2 + 6xz^2$
17. $18xy^2 + 2y^3$
18. $8ab^2 - 16a^2b$

Factor each polynomial.

19. $15x^3 + 24$
20. $12x^3y^2 - 15x^2y$
21. $15d^2 - 25d + 30$
22. $ax^3 + 5bx^3 + 9cx^3$
23. $3x^3y + 9xy^2 + 36xy$
24. $15y^2 + 9x^3$
25. $x^2y + x^3y$
26. $18x^3y^2 + 12xy^3$
27. $28x^5y - 21x^2y^6$
28. $28m^2 + 18m$
29. $21xy^5 + 35x^3y$
30. $45a^3c^8 - 72a^5c^3$
31. $36a^2b^3 - 45ab^4$
32. $12axy - 14ay + 20ax$
33. $24x^2y^2 + 12xy + x$
34. $rst + rw + tr$
35. $14a^3x + 19a^3y + 11a^3z$
36. $a + a^2b^2 + a^3b^3$
37. $27a^2x + 9ax^2$
38. $3x^2y + 6xy + 9y^2$
39. $28a^2b^2c^2 + 14abc - 21a^2bc^2$
40. $42abc - 12a^2b^2 + 3a^2c^2$
41. $15mn^2 + 20m^2$
42. $12x^2y^2z^2 - 48xyz^3$
43. $2a^3b^2 + 8ab + 16a^2b^3$
44. $6x^2 + 9xy + 24x^2y^2$
45. $11a^2b^2 - 14ab^2$
46. $14xy^2 - 2xy$
47. $12xy^3 + y^4$
48. $11a^2b^2 + 14ab^2$
49. $14abc + 18ab$
50. $3a^2b - 6a^2b^2$
51. $12x^2y^2z^2 + 48xyz^3$

4.12 Factoring the Difference of Squares

You can find the product of the binomials $x + 3$ and $x - 3$ by using the FOIL process.

$$\begin{array}{c} \quad\text{F}\quad\text{O}\quad\text{I}\quad\text{L} \\ (x+3)(x-3) = x^2 - 3x + 3x - 9 \quad \textit{The two middle terms drop out because} \\ = x^2 - 9 \qquad\qquad -3x + 3x = 0. \end{array}$$

Notice that x^2 is the square of x and 9 is the square of 3.
Thus, the product is the **difference of two squares**.
In general, the product of the sum and difference of two numbers is equal to the difference of their squares.

$$\boxed{(a+b)(a-b) = a^2 - b^2}$$

By reversing the process, you can factor the difference of two squares.

Example 1 Factor $9y^2 - 49$.

$$\begin{array}{ll} a^2 - b^2 = (a+b)(a-b) & \\ 9y^2 - 49 = (3y)^2 - (7)^2 & \quad 3y \cdot 3y = 9y^2 \text{ and } 7 \cdot 7 = 49 \\ = (3y+7)(3y-7) & \end{array}$$

An expression always should be factored completely.
Sometimes a common factor can be factored from a binomial.

Example 2 Factor $50a^2 - 128b^2$.

$$\begin{array}{ll} 50a^2 - 128b^2 = 2(25a^2 - 64b^2) & \quad \textit{The GCF of } 50a^2 \textit{ and } 128b^2 \textit{ is 2.} \\ = 2[(5a)^2 - (8b)^2] & \\ = 2(5a+8b)(5a-8b) & \end{array}$$

Find each product.

1. $(y-1)(y+1)$ **2.** $(2+a)(2-a)$ **3.** $(5a-2y)(5a+2y)$

4. $(3x-2)(3x+2)$ **5.** $(x+5)(x-5)$ **6.** $(ab+7)(ab-7)$

7. $(x^2-9)(x^2+9)$ **8.** $3(8r+1)(8r-1)$ **9.** $(mn-4)(mn+4)$

Determine whether each of the following is a difference of squares. Write yes or no.

10. $d^2 - 12$ **11.** $(a^2-b)(a^2+b)$ **12.** $(a+b)(a-b)$

13. $(d+7)(d-7)$ **14.** $(a-b)(a-b)$ **15.** $c^2 - 16$

16. $(x+y)(x-y)$ **17.** $m^2 + 9$ **18.** $m^2n^2 - 9$

Factor each of the following.

19. $4x^2 - 9y^2$ **20.** $64m^2 - 25n^2$ **21.** $a^2 - 9$

22. $9x^2 - 25y^2$ **23.** $1 - 25c^2$ **24.** $25y^2 - 49w^2$

25. $64a^2 - 4b^2$ **26.** $25x^2y^4 - 64x^4y^4$ **27.** $16a^2b^2 - c^2d^2$

28. $8m^2 - 72n^2$ **29.** $192a^2 - 75b^2$ **30.** $36x^2y^2 - 81m^2$

4.13 Factoring Algebraic Expressions of the Form $ax^2 + bx + c$

The following polynomials are in, or can be changed into, the form $ax^2 + bx + c$. Then each is shown in factored form.

$6x^2 - 2x \longrightarrow 6x^2 - 2x + 0 \qquad 2x(3x - 1)$

$169x^2 - 100 \longrightarrow 169x^2 + 0 \cdot x - 100 \qquad (13x + 10)(13x - 10)$

$x^2 + 7x + 10 \longrightarrow 1 \cdot x^2 + 7x + 10 \qquad (x + 2)(x + 5)$

You can find the product of $x + 2$ and $x + 5$ with the FOIL method. Notice the pattern in multiplication.

$$\begin{array}{c} \text{F O I L} \\ (x+2)(x+5) = x^2 + 5x + 2x + 10 \\ \text{F O I L} \\ = x^2 + (5+2)x + 10 \\ = x^2 + \quad 7x + 10 \end{array} \qquad \begin{array}{c} \text{F O I L} \\ (x+m)(x+n) = x^2 + nx + mx + mn \\ \text{F O I L} \\ = x^2 + (n+m)x + mn \end{array}$$

You can use this pattern to factor some other polynomials of the form $ax^2 + bx + c$.

Example 1 Factor $x^2 + 7x + 10$.

To factor $x^2 + 7x + 10$ into the form $(x + m)(x + n)$, you must find the numbers m and n whose sum is 7 and whose product is 10. That is, find m and n such that $m + n = 7$ and $m \cdot n = 10$. List the factors of 10 first. Then find their sums.

Factors of 10	Sum of Factors
1, 10	1 + 10 = 11
−1, −10	−1 + (−10) = −11
2, 5	**2 + 5 = 7**
−2, −5	−2 + (−5) = −7

The factors you are seeking are 2 and 5. Thus, $(x + 2)(x + 5)$ is the factored form of $x^2 + 7x + 10$. You can check the answer by multiplying the two factors.

Example 2 Factor $r^2 - 3r - 4$.

List the factors of −4. The two whose sum is −3 are the ones you are seeking.

Factors of −4	Sum of Factors
1, −4	**1 + (−4) = −3**
−1, 4	−1 + 4 = 3
2, −2	2 + (−2) = 0

In factored form, $r^2 - 3r - 4$ is $(r + 1)(r - 4)$.

Example 3 Factor $2x^2 - 7x + 6$.

The coefficient of x^2 is not 1. The factors of $2x^2 + 7x + 6$ are of the following form.

Factors of 2   Factors of 6
first   last

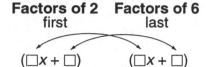

$(\Box x + \Box) \qquad (\Box x + \Box)$

First, find the factors of 2 and 6
Factors of 2: 2, 1   Factors of 6: 6, 1
              −2, −1   −6, −1
                                            2, 3
                                            −2, −3

Now list the possible factors of $2x^2 - 7x + 6$.

Possible Factors	Outer + Inner Terms
$(2x + 6)(x + 1)$	$2x + 6x = 8x$
$(x + 6)(2x + 1)$	$x + 12x = 13x$
$(2x − 6)(x − 1)$	$−2x − 6x = −8x$
$(x − 6)(2x − 1)$	$−x − 12x = −13x$
$(2x + 2)(x + 3)$	$6x + 2x = 8x$
$(x + 2)(2x + 3)$	$3x + 4x = 7x$
$(2x − 2)(x − 3)$	$−6x − 2x = −8x$
$(x − 2)(2x − 3)$ √	$−3x − 4x = −7x$ √

Therefore, $2x^2 - 7x + 6 - (x\ 2)(2x - 3)$.

For each exercise in the following table, find two integers with the product and sum indicated.
Sample: Product = 72, sum = 18. The integers are 6 and 12 since
            $6 \cdot 12 = 72$ and $6 + 12 = 18$.

Exercise	1	2	3	4	5	6
Product	2	10	13	−5	49	−12
Sum	3	7	14	−4	14	1

Complete the factoring in each exercise.

7. $y^2 - 8y + 12 = (y - \Box)(y - 6)$

8. $p^2 - 2p - 63 = (p\ \Box\ 7)(p\ \Box\ 9)$

9. $2x^2 + 5x + 3 = (2x + \Box)(x + 1)$

10. $x^2 - 6x + 5 = (x - 1)(x - \Box)$

Factor each polynomial.

11. $m^2 + 16m + 63$ **12.** $x^2 - 14x + 45$ **13.** $n^2 + 19n + 84$

14. $b^2 - 20b + 96$ **15.** $a^2 - 7a + 12$ **16.** $a^2 + 5a - 66$

17. $n^2 - 2n - 15$ **18.** $m^2 + 3m - 18$ **19.** $5x^2 + 9x - 18$

20. $d^2 + 12d + 20$ **21.** $p^2 + 11p + 28$ **22.** $s^2 - 7s + 10$

23. $y^2 - 13y + 30$ **24.** $5c^2 + 23c + 12$ **25.** $6x^2 - 11x - 35$

26. $x^2 + 12x + 36$ **27.** $c^2 + 14c + 45$ **28.** $15k^2 - 17k - 42$

29. $3m^2 + 7m - 20$ **30.** $x^2 + 12x + 27$ **31.** $d^2 - 8cd + 15c^2$

32. $a^2 + 8a + 15$ **33.** $a^2 - 22a + 21$ **34.** $y^2 - 11y + 30$

35. $y^2 + 9y + 14$ **36.** $48 + 14p + p^2$ **37.** $66 + 17m + m^2$

38. $15 - 8r + r^2$ **39.** $x^2 - 17x + 72$ **40.** $m^2 - 15m + 26$

41. $36 + 13y + y^2$ **42.** $m^2 - 9m + 20$ **43.** $a^2 + 7a + 10$

44. $16 + 10d + d^2$ **45.** $90 - 19x + x^2$ **46.** $13 - 14t + t^2$

47. $18 - 9c + c^2$ **48.** $p^2 - 19p + 60$ **49.** $x^2 + 6x + 8$

CHAPTER 4   SOLUTIONS and ANSWERS

Section 4.1

1. yes, −10
2. no
3. yes, 21
4. yes, −1
5. yes, 1
6. yes, $\frac{2}{5}$
7. no
8. yes, $-\frac{1}{17}$
9. no
10. no
11. 2
12. 2
13. 3
14. 7
15. 1
16. $(-3 + -11)xy = -14xy$
17. $(-19 + 8)y = -11y$
18. Monomials are dissimilar.
19. $(16 + 2)x^2 = 18x^2$
20. $(3 - 5)ab = -2ab$
21. $(6 + 3 + 9)x^3 = 18x^3$
22. $(2 - 3)y^3 = -y^3$
23. Monomials are dissimilar.
24. $(4 - 1)mn = 3mn$
25. $\frac{9}{6}x^3$ or $1\frac{1}{2}x^3$
26. $(5 - 7 + 12)ab = 10ab$
27. $\left(5 - \frac{1}{3} + 4\right)y = 8\frac{2}{3}y$

Section 4.2

1. $3x$
2. $-7ab$
3. $-a$
4. $-4y^2$
5. -9
6. $10xy$
7. $5z$
8. $-41x$
9. $(66 + -28)(xy) = 38xy$
   Check.
   $38xy + 28xy = (38 + 28)xy$
   $\qquad\qquad = 66xy$
10. $(75 + -17)xyz = 58xyz$
    Check.
    $58xyz + 17xyz = (58 + 17)xyz$
    $\qquad\qquad\quad = 75xyz$
11. $353 + -272 = 81$
    Check.
    $81 + 272 = 353$
    $\qquad 353 = 353$
12. $(48 + -27)y^2 = 21y^2$
    Check.
    $21y^2 + 27y^2 = (21 + 27)y^2$
    $\qquad\qquad\quad = 48y^2$
13. $(26 + -25)a^2b = a^2b$
    Check.
    $a^2b + 25a^2b = (1 + 25)a^2b$
    $\qquad\qquad\quad = 26a^2b$
14. $(41 + 16)x^2y^3 = 57x^2y^3$
    Check.
    $57x^2y^3 + -16x^2y^3 = (57 + -16)x^2y^3$
    $\qquad\qquad\qquad\quad = 41x^2y^3$

The checks for 15 - 24 are done as above, but will not be shown.

15. $(7 + 10)xy^2 = 17xy^2$
16. $(51 + -1)ab^2 = 50ab^2$
17. $(54 + 22)abc = 76abc$
18. $(28 + 21)c^2d^2 = 49c^2d^2$
19. $444 + 69 = 513$
20. $(14 + -13)x^2y^3z = x^2y^3z$
21. $(45 + 1)rst^2 = 46rst^2$
22. $\left(\frac{x}{2} + -\frac{x}{4}\right)y^2 = \frac{x}{4}y^2$
23. $\left(\frac{2}{3} + \frac{1}{6}\right)cd^2 = \frac{5}{6}cd^2$
24. $(101 + 11)a^3b^2c = 112a^3b^2c$

Section 4.3

1. 3125
2. 27
3. 8
4. 1296
5. 128
6. 64
7. 16
8. −128
9. 9216
10. 1024
11. 20,736
12. 36
13. $-4abc$
14. $-8x^3$
15. $c^2 \cdot c^2 = c^4$
16. $y^4 \cdot y^7 = y^{11}$
17. $18xy^2$
18. $x^2 \cdot x^5 = x^7$
19. $y^3 \cdot y^3 = y^6$
20. $x^6 \cdot x \cdot x^3 = x^{10}$
21. $d \cdot d^4 = d^5$
22. $(8a^2b^3)(3b^4) = 24a^2b^7$
23. $(x^2y^2)(xy^3) = x^3y^5$
24. $(xy)(10x^2) = 10x^3y$
25. $(7c^2d^3)(-4c^5d^6) = -28c^7d^9$
26. $(7x^2y^4)(12x^6y^8) = 84x^8y^{12}$
27. $(8c^2d^4)(-5c^6d^2) = -40c^8d^6$
28. $(9c^9d^8)(12c^5d^2) = 108c^{14}d^{10}$
29. $(8c^5d^7)(13c^2d^8) = 104c^7d^{15}$
30. $(6w^3z^4)(-3w^2z^5)(8w^9z^8) = -144w^{14}z^{17}$
31. $(3w^2v)(-2w^5v^2)(4w^6v^5) = -24w^{13}v^8$
32. $(-2w^2v^7)(-4w^3v^2) = 8w^5v^9$
33. $(8x^3y^2z^6)(-9x^9y^6z^5) = -72x^{12}y^8z^{11}$
34. $(m^3)^2 = m^6$
35. $(n^3)^9 = n^{27}$
36. $(a^2)^3 = a^6$
37. $(4a)^2 = 16a^2$
38. $(x^3)^4 = x^{12}$
39. $(-2y)^5 = -32y^5$
40. $(-4x^6y^4z^8)^3 = -64x^{18}y^{12}z^{24}$
41. $(xy)^7 = x^7y^7$
42. $(3a^2)^6 = 729a^{12}$
43. $(x^3y^5)^2 = x^6y^{10}$

44. $(-6x^5y^3z^9)^3 = -216x^{15}y^9z^{27}$ **45.** $(-3x^3y^2z^5)^4 = 81x^{12}y^8z^{20}$

Section 4.4

1. 4   **2.** 64   **3.** 3   **4.** $\dfrac{1}{6}$ **5.** 1   **6.** 64   **7.** $\dfrac{1}{25}$ **8.** $\dfrac{4}{5}$

9. y **10.** a^4 **11.** $\dfrac{1}{b^4}$ **12.** x^{-5} **13.** an^3 **14.** y^3 **15.** $-x^3t^3$ **16.** $-\dfrac{1}{a^2b^4}$

17. $\dfrac{7st^2}{r}$ **18.** $3b^2$ **19.** $\dfrac{9m^2}{n^5}$ **20.** $\dfrac{9b^3}{c^3}$ **21.** $\dfrac{12d^6}{c^8}$ **22.** $\dfrac{m^3}{4}$ **23.** $\dfrac{9m^2}{n^5}$ **24.** $\dfrac{rs^6}{-5}$

25. $\dfrac{y^5}{4x^5}$ **26.** $\dfrac{3x^{10}}{2y^2}$ **27.** $\dfrac{6c^3}{5d}$ **28.** $\dfrac{x^3}{-7y^5}$ **29.** $\dfrac{1}{3b^5c^3}$ **30.** $\dfrac{1}{3abc^2}$ **31.** $\dfrac{c^5d^2f^3}{5}$ **32.** $\dfrac{1}{4xy^2}$

33. $-7s^6$ **34.** n^4m^2 **35.** $-\dfrac{1}{8ab}$ **36.** $\dfrac{a^3b}{5}$ **37.** $\dfrac{-1}{4y^4}$ **38.** $\dfrac{1}{8bc}$ **39.** $\dfrac{4}{11yz^7}$ **40.** $\dfrac{1}{6bc^3}$

41. $\dfrac{1}{b^2}$ **42.** $\dfrac{-ab^4}{12}$ **43.** $\dfrac{z^4}{5x^4y}$ **44.** $\dfrac{c^2d^8f^3}{5}$ **45.** $\dfrac{1}{bc^3}$ **46.** $\dfrac{-1}{4ab^4c^5}$ **47.** $\dfrac{cd^2}{5}$ **48.** $\dfrac{ac}{4}$

Section 4.5

1. 6.8×10^3 **2.** 5.3×10^5 **3.** 9.5×10^{-3} **4.** 2.5×10^{-7}

5. 7×10^4 **6.** 8.8×10^{10} **7.** 1×10^8 **8.** 9.6×10^{-4}

9. 3×10^{-3} **10.** 7.7×10^{-4} **11.** 2.3×10^7 **12.** 1.56×10^{-13}

13. 6×10^{10} **14.** 1.225×10^{10} **15.** 1.29×10^{-1} **16.** 8×10^{12}

17. 1.5×10^{-11} **18.** 5.427×10^{-4} **19.** 2.464×10^7 **20.** 3.24×10^9

21. 3.22×10^{-4} **22.** 1.927×10^{-7} **23.** 1.664×10^7 **24.** 1.353×10^1

25. 2.7×10^{-8} **26.** 3×10^{15} **27.** 1.6×10^{-6} **28.** 6.4×10^{-3}

29. 1.8×10^2 **30.** 1.5×10^5 **31.** 8.4×10^{-1} **32.** 4.2×10^{10}

Section 4.6

1. $2x^5$: 5   **2.** $6x^5$: 5   **3.** $3x^4$: 4

4. $6x^3y^5$: 8   **5.** $5z^5$: 5   **6.** $8x^4y^3$: 7

7. $-6x^3 + 11x^2 + 9x - 1$ **8.** $-5x^3 + 3x^2 + 28x - 2$ **9.** $18x^3 + 3x^2 - 2x - 7$

10. $\begin{aligned}(19n - 7m) + (10n - 3m) &= (19n + 10n) + (-7m - 3m) \\ &= (19 + 10)n + (-7 - 3)m \\ &= 29n - 10m\end{aligned}$

11. $\begin{aligned}(5x^2 - 5x + 2) + (-3x^2 - 4x - 1) &= (5x^2 + -3x^2) + (-5x - 4x) + (2 - 1) \\ &= (5 - 3)x^2 + (-5 - 4)x + 1 \\ &= 2x^2 - 9x + 1\end{aligned}$

12. $\begin{aligned}(9x - 2y) + (4x + 4y) &= (9x + 4x) + (-2y + 4y) \\ &= (9 + 4)x + (-2 + 4)y \\ &= 13x + 2y\end{aligned}$

13. $\begin{aligned}(6m^2 + m - 9) + (-6m^2 + 6m + 9) &= (6m^2 - 6m^2) + (m + 6m) + (-9 + 9) \\ &= (6 - 6)m^2 + (1 + 6)m - 0 \\ &= 7m\end{aligned}$

14. $\begin{aligned}(9w^2 + 3w - 8) + (6w^2 - 5w + 5) &= (9w^2 + 6w^2) + (3w - 5w) + (-8 + 5) \\ &= (9 + 6)w^2 + (3 - 5)w - 3 \\ &= 15w^2 - 2w - 3\end{aligned}$

15. $\begin{array}{r} 5a^2 - 6a + 5 \\ + \ 9a^2 + 3a - 9 \\ \hline 14a^2 - 3a - 4 \end{array}$

16. $\begin{array}{r} 13c^2 + 4c - 9 \\ + \ 3c^2 - 9c + 8 \\ \hline 16c^2 - 5c - 1 \end{array}$

17. $9y^2 - 5y$

18. $-x^2 + 35xy - 9y^2$

19. $7y^3 - 4xy^2 + 15x^2y + 11$

20. $4x^2 - 3x - 1$

21. $5x$

22. $-a$

23. $-4x - 2y$

24. $-4ab$

25. $-a + b$

26. $-x^3 + x + 1$

27. $9m^2 - 3m - 1$

28. $8x - 11$

29. $-2a^2 - 3b + 1$

30.
$$\begin{array}{llll} 6x - y & \text{multiply subtrahend} \rightarrow & 6x - y & \text{Check:} & -x - 4y & \text{Difference} \\ \underline{-(7x + 3y)} & \text{by } -1 & \underline{-7x - 3y} & & \underline{7x + 3y} & \text{Subtrahend} \\ & & -x - 4y & & 6x - y & \text{Minuend} \end{array}$$

31.
$$\begin{array}{lllll} 9w^2 + 5w - 8 & & 9w^2 + 5w - 8 & \text{Check.} & 3w^2 - 3w + 1 & \text{Difference} \\ \underline{-(6w^2 + 8w - 9)} & \rightarrow & \underline{-6w^2 - 8w + 9} & & \underline{6w^2 + 8w - 9} & \text{Subtrahend} \\ & & 3w^2 - 3w + 1 & & 9w^2 + 5w - 8 & \text{Minuend} \end{array}$$

32.
$$\begin{aligned} (2a + 10b) - (a - 4b) &= (2a + 10b) + (-1)(a - 4b) \\ &= (2a + 10b) + (-a + 4b) \\ &= (2a - a) + (10b + 4b) \\ &= a + 14b \end{aligned}$$
Check: $(a + 14b) + (a - 4b) \stackrel{?}{=} 2a + 10b$ Add difference and subtrahend
$$2a + 10b = 2a + 10b$$

33.
$$\begin{aligned} (5x^2 + 6x - 9) - (3x^2 - 4x + 8) &= (5x^2 + 6x - 9) + (-1)(3x^2 - 4x + 8) \\ &= (5x^2 + 6x - 9) + (-3x^2 + 4x - 8) \\ &= (5x^2 - 3x^2) + (6x + 4x) + (-9 - 8) \\ &= 2x^2 + 10x - 17 \end{aligned}$$

34.
$$\begin{array}{lllll} 6x^2 + 4x - 5 & & 6x^2 + 4x - 5 & \text{Check.} & -3x^2 + 7x - 7 & \text{Difference} \\ \underline{-(9x^2 - 3x + 2)} & \rightarrow & \underline{-9x^2 + 3x - 2} & & \underline{9x^2 - 3x + 2} & \text{Subtrahend} \\ & & -3x^2 + 7x - 7 & & 6x^2 + 4x - 5 & \text{Minuend} \end{array}$$

35. $2a^2 - 2a - 7$

36. $5b^2 - 3b - 24$

37. $5y^2 - 8xy + 2x^2$

38. $7c^2 + 11c - 11$

39. $9c^2 + 13c - 32$

40. $x^2y^2 + 3xy - 28$

Section 4.7

1. $3a^3 + 3ab$

2. $x^3 - 4x^2$

3. $3ro - 0r^2$

4. $12x^3 - 8x^3y$

5. $-9x^2 + 15xy$

6. $25x - 5x^2$

7. $16n^3 + 40n^2 + 40n$

8. $60m^3 - 42m^2 + 36m$

9. $15n^4 - 25n^3 + 5n^2$

10. $28ay^2 - 28a^2y + 20a^3$

11. $2a^2b^4 + 8a^3b^3 + 2a^4b$

12. $15x^5y^2 - 15x^3y^2 + 6x^4y^3$

13. $x(x + 5) + 6(x + 5)$

14. $3y(y + 2) + 2(y + 2)$

15. $x(3x - 4) + 7(3x - 4)$

16. $5a(5a - 3) - 8(5a - 3)$

17. $(x + 6)(x + 9)$ Innerterms: $6x$

18. $(x + 7)(x - 6)$ Outer terms: $-6x$

19. $(x + 5)(x + 7)$ Last terms: 35

20. $(x + 2)(x - 21)$ First terms: x^2

21. $(a - 2)(a + 1)$ Outer terms: a

22. $(11 + y)(7 - y)$ Last terms: $-y^2$

23.
$$\begin{aligned} (a - 3)(a + 5) &= a^2 + 5a - 3a - 15 \\ &= a^2 + 2a - 15 \end{aligned}$$

24.
$$\begin{aligned} (x + 3)(x - 3) &= x^2 - 3x + 3x - 9 \\ &= x^2 - 9 \end{aligned}$$

25.
$$\begin{aligned} (2x - 5)(3x + 4) &= 6x^2 + 8x - 15x - 20 \\ &= 6x^2 - 7x - 20 \end{aligned}$$

26.
$$\begin{aligned} (y + 2)(y + 7) &= y^2 + 7y + 2y + 14 \\ &= y^2 + 9y + 14 \end{aligned}$$

27. $6x^2 + 3x - 30$

28. $6x^2 - 8x - 30$

29. $12x^2 + 7x - 45$

30. $24x^2 - 38x - 7$

31. $16x^2 - 25$

32. $8x^2 + 2x - 21$

33. $56x^2 - 59x + 15$

34. $25m^2 + 60mn + 36n^2$

35. $6x^2 - 11x - 35$

36. $c^2 + 10c + 25$

37. $9x^2 - 36x + 36$

38. $x^3 + 5x^2 + 10x + 8$

39. $x^5 - x^2 + x - 1$

40. $x^3 + 5x^2 + 7x + 3$

41. $2x^3 + 3x^2 + 3x + 1$

42. $-2x^2y + 12x^2y^2 + 3xy^2 - 8xy^3 - 15y^4$

43. $27x^3 + 54x^2y + 36xy^2 + 8y^3$

44. $9x^4 - 54x^3 + 32x^2$

Section 4.8

1. $\dfrac{4^5}{4^4} = 4^{5-4}$ or 4^1 or 4

2. $\dfrac{y^8}{y^2} = y^{8-2}$ or y^6

3. $\dfrac{6y^2 + 4}{2} = \dfrac{6y^2}{2} + \dfrac{4}{2} = 3y^2 + 2$

4. $\dfrac{11b^3 + b}{b} = \dfrac{11b^3}{b} + \dfrac{b}{b} = 11b^2 + 1$

5. $\dfrac{15x^8}{5x^5} = 3x^{8-5}$ or $3x^3$

6. $\dfrac{44a^7}{11a} = 4a^6$

7. $\dfrac{b^2c^2}{4} - 2bc$

8. $\dfrac{12c^2 - 4c}{4c} = \dfrac{12c^2}{4c} - \dfrac{4c}{4c} = 3c - 1$

9. $3rs + 1 - 4r$

10. $7q - 5 + 2p$

11. $-7x^3 - 9x + 12$

12. $a^3b - a + \dfrac{2}{b}$

13. $-7xy^4 + 5xy^3 + 3$

14. $a^2b - a + 4$

15. $\dfrac{4cd^2}{3} - \dfrac{2d^4f}{3c} + \dfrac{2}{f}$

16. $2x^2y^4 + 3x^2 + 6y^2$

17. $\dfrac{5a^6b^4c^3}{4} + \dfrac{3a^4c}{4} - \dfrac{1}{4b}$

18. $\dfrac{z}{6x} - \dfrac{4yz^2}{3x} + 2$

19. $\dfrac{1}{rs^2t} + \dfrac{8}{rs} - 2t$

20. $5a - 2a^3b^2c + 6c^9$

21. $7rs - 7 - \dfrac{t^5}{2}$

22. $3yz + \dfrac{6y}{z^2} - xy^2$

23. $\dfrac{1}{ab} + \dfrac{3}{a^2} - \dfrac{bd}{2c}$

24. $3y + \dfrac{5yz}{x} + \dfrac{2}{x}$

25. $\dfrac{1}{2abc} + \dfrac{10c}{b} + \dfrac{3c^2}{ab^2}$

26. $4xy + 6yz^2 + 8xy^4z^2$

Section 4.9

1. $x + 2$

2. $x^2 - 2x + 3$

3. $y + 1$

4. $4m^2 - 6m + 9$

5. $b - 2$

6. $t^2 + 4t - 3$ R-3

7. $s + 2$

8. $3d^2 + 2d + 3$ R-2

9. $y^3 + 3y^2 + 9y + 27$

10. $x^2 - 4x + 17$

11. $x + 4$

12. $3y + 7$

13. $5t + 2$

14. $m + 5 - \dfrac{33}{2m + 3}$

15. $x + 4$

16. $x^3 + 2x^2 + 9x + 8$

17. $7y - 19 + \dfrac{48}{2y + 3}$

18. $x^2 + 2x - 4$

19. $x^3 - x^2 + x - 1$

20. $x^7 + 2x^6 + 4x^5 + 8x^4 + 16x^3 + 32x^2 + 64x + 128$

21. $x^3 + 3x - 1$

Section 4.10

1. b

2. a

3. f

4. c

5. d

6. $40: 2 \cdot 2 \cdot 2 \cdot 5$

7. $68: 2 \cdot 2 \cdot 17$

8. $21: 3 \cdot 7$

9. $60: 2 \cdot 2 \cdot 3 \cdot 5$

10. $-12: -1 \cdot 2 \cdot 2 \cdot 3$

11. $80: 2 \cdot 2 \cdot 2 \cdot 2 \cdot 5$

12. $-26: -1 \cdot 2 \cdot 13$

13. $304: 2 \cdot 2 \cdot 2 \cdot 2 \cdot 19$

14. $-96: -1 \cdot 2 \cdot 2 \cdot 2 \cdot 2 \cdot 2 \cdot 3$

15. $-112: -1 \cdot 2 \cdot 2 \cdot 2 \cdot 2 \cdot 7$

16. $5005: 5 \cdot 7 \cdot 11 \cdot 13$

17. $75: 3 \cdot 5 \cdot 5$

18. $81: 3 \cdot 3 \cdot 3 \cdot 3$

19. $15: 3 \cdot 5$
    $24: 2 \cdot 2 \cdot 2 \cdot 3$
    gcf: 3

20. $4: 2 \cdot 2$
    $12: 2 \cdot 2 \cdot 3$
    gcf: $2 \cdot 2$ or 4

21. 3

22. 6

23. 11

24. 126

25. 24

26. 4

27. 9

28. 4

29. 13

30. 5

31. 19

32. 2

33. 6

34. 4

35. 4

36. 6

37. 7

38. 10

39. 4

40. 7

41. 6

42. 2

43. 2

44. 8

45. 1

46. 6

47. 5

48. 16

49. 2

Section 4.11

1. $22y^2: 2 \cdot 11 \cdot y \cdot y$
   $33y^3: 3 \cdot 11 \cdot y \cdot y \cdot y$
   GCF: $11y^2$

2. $-25ab: -1 \cdot 5 \cdot 5 \cdot a \cdot b$
   $35: 5 \cdot 7$
   GCF: 5

3. $10x^2: 2 \cdot 5 \cdot x \cdot x$
   $35x: 5 \cdot 7 \cdot x$
   GCF: $5x$

4. $6rst$ 5. $3m^2n^3$ 6. $27a^2b$ 7. 2 8. 4 9. $3xy^2$ 10. $14b$

11. $3xy$ 12. 9 13. $2c$ 14. xy 15. $7y$ 16. $2x$ 17. $2y^2$

18. $8ab$ 19. $3(5x^3+8)$ 20. $3x^2y(4xy-5)$ 21. $5(3d^2-5d+6)$

22. $x^3(a+5b+9c)$ 23. $3xy(x^2+3y+12)$ 24. $3(5y^2+3x^3)$ 25. $x^2y(1+x)$

26. $6xy^2(3x^2+2y)$ 27. $7x^2y(4x^3-3y^5)$ 28. $2m(14m+9)$ 29. $7xy(3y^4+5x^2)$

30. $9a^3c^3(5c^5-8a^2)$ 31. $9ab^3(4a-5b)$ 32. $2a(6xy-7y+10x)$ 33. $x(24xy^2+12y+1)$

34. $r(st+w+t)$ 35. $a^3(14x+19y+11z)$ 36. $a(1+ab^2+a^2b^3)$ 37. $9ax(3a+x)$

38. $3y(x^2+2x+3y)$ 39. $7abc(4abc+2-3ac)$ 40. $3a(14bc-4ab^2+ac^2)$ 41. $5m(3n^2+4m)$

42. $12xyz^2(xy-4z)$ 43. $2ab(a^2b+4+8ab^2)$ 44. $3x(2x+3y+8xy^2)$ 45. $ab^2(11a-14)$

46. $2xy(7y-1)$ 47. $y^3(12x+y)$ 48. $ab^2(11a+14)$ 49. $2ab(7c+9)$

50. $3a^2b(1-2b)$ 51. $12xyz^2(xy+4z)$

Section 4.12

1. y^2-1 2. $4-a^2$ 3. $25a^2-4y^2$

4. $9x^2-4$ 5. x^2-25 6. a^2b^2-49

7. x^4-81 8. $192r^2-3$ 9. m^2n^2-16

10. d^2-12; no, 12 is not a square.   11. $(a^2-b)(a^2+b)$; yes   12. $(a+b)(a-b)$; yes

13. $(d+7)(d-7)$; yes   14. $(a-b)(a-b)$; no, one factor is not a sum.

15. c^2-16; yes   16. $(x+y)(x-y)$; yes   17. m^2+9; no, it's a sum

18. m^2n^2-9; yes   19. $(2x-3y)(2x+3y)$ 20. $(8m-5n)(8m+5n)$

21. $(a+3)(a-3)$ 22. $(3x+5y)(3x-5y)$ 23. $(1+5c)(1-5c)$

24. $(5y-7w)(5y+7w)$ 25. $(8a+2b)(8a-2b)$ 26. $(5xy^2+8x^2y^2)(5xy^2-8x^2y^2)$

27. $(4ab+cd)(4ab-cd)$ 28. $8(m-3n)(m+3n)$ 29. $3(8a+5b)(8a-5b)$

30. $9(2xy-3m)(2xy+3m)$

Section 4.13

1. $1, 2$ 2. $2, 5$ 3. $1, 13$

4. $-5, 1$ 5. $7, 7$ 6. $-3, 4$

7. $(y-2)(y-6)$ 8. $(p+7)(p-9)$ 9. $(2x+3)(x+1)$

10. $(x-1)(x-5)$ 11. $(m+7)(m+9)$ 12. $(x-5)(x-9)$

13. $(n+12)(n+7)$ 14. $(b-12)(b-8)$ 15. $(a-3)(a-4)$

16. $(a+11)(a-6)$ 17. $(n+3)(n-5)$ 18. $(m+6)(m-3)$

19. $(5x-6)(x+3)$ 20. $(d+10)(d+2)$ 21. $(p+7)(p+4)$

22. $(s-5)(s-2)$ 23. $(y-10)(y-3)$ 24. $(5c+3)(c+4)$

25. $(3x+5)(2x-7)$ 26. $(x+6)(x+6)$ 27. $(c+9)(c+5)$

28. $(5k+6)(3k-7)$ 29. $(3m-5)(m+4)$ 30. $(x+9)(x+3)$

31. $(d-5c)(d-3c)$ 32. $(a+3)(a+5)$ 33. $(a-21)(a-1)$

34. $(y-5)(y-6)$ 35. $(y+7)(y+2)$ 36. $(p+6)(p+8)$

37. $(m+11)(m+6)$ 38. $(r-5)(r-3)$ 39. $(x-9)(x-8)$

40. $(m-13)(m-2)$ 41. $(y+9)(y+4)$ 42. $(m-5)(m-4)$

43. $(a+5)(a+2)$ 44. $(d+8)(d+2)$ 45. $(x-10)(x-9)$

46. $(t-13)(t-1)$ 47. $(c-6)(c-3)$ 48. $(p-15)(p-4)$

49. $(x+4)(x+2)$

CHAPTER 5   QUADRATIC EQUATIONS AND SYSTEMS OF EQUATIONS

5.1   Solving Quadratic Equations

An equation of one variable is **quadratic** if 2 is the greatest exponent of the variable in the equation. Examples are $x^2 = 9$ and $x^2 - 3x + 2 = 0$.

Example 1   Solve $x^2 = 9$.

$$x^2 = 9$$
$x = \pm\sqrt{9}$ *Find the square root of each side of the equation.*
$x = \pm 3$ *The sign, $\pm$, means positive or negative.*
There are two solutions, 3 and –3.

Check $x^2 = 9$ $x^2 = 9$

$(3)^2 \stackrel{?}{=} 9$ $(-3)^2 \stackrel{?}{=} 9$

$9 = 9$ $9 = 9$

In example 1 we solved the equation by finding the square root of each side. You can see that another method is needed to solve equations such that $x^2 - 3x + 2 = 0$. Consider the following products.

$$7 \cdot 0 = 0 \qquad 0(-4) = 0 \qquad 0 \cdot 0 = 0$$

From these examples and many more, you can conclude that if any product equals 0, then at least one factor is 0. This is called **zero product property**. It is written in symbols as follows.

> **For all numbers a and b,**
> $ab = 0$ **if and only if** $a = 0$ **or** $b = 0$.

The following example shows that you can use this property to solve some quadratic equations.

Example 2   Solve $x^2 - 3x + 2 = 0$.

$$x^2 - 3x + 2 = 0$$
$(x - 2)(x - 1) = 0$ *Factor the polynomial on the left side.*
From the zero product property, you know either of the following must be true.

$(x - 2) = 0$ or $(x - 1) = 0$
Solve each equation. $x - 2 + 2 = 2$ $x - 1 + 1 = 1$
$x = 2$ $x = 1$
There are two solutions, 2 and 1.

Check: $x^2 - 3x + 2 = 0$ $x^2 - 3x + 2 = 0$

$(2)^2 - 3(2) + 2 \stackrel{?}{=} 0$ $(1)^2 - 3(1) + 2 \stackrel{?}{=} 0$

$0 = 0$ $1 - 3 + 2 \stackrel{?}{=} 0$

$0 = 0$

The equation $x^2 - 3x + 2 = 0$ is a **quadratic equation in standard form** because it is a quadratic polynomial in standard form which equals 0.

Use the following steps to solve a quadratic equation by factoring.

1. Write the equation in standard form.
2. Factor the quadratic polynomial.
3. Set each factor equal to 0 using the zero product property.
4. Solve each resulting equation.
5. Check the solutions in the original equation.

Example 3 Solve $2x^2 = 16x$.

$$2x^2 = 16$$

1. Write the equation in standard form $2x^2 - 16x = 16x - 16x$
   by subtracting $16x$ from both sides. $2x^2 - 16x = 0$
2. Factor the polynmial. $2x(x-8) = 0$
3. Set each factor equal to 0. $2x = 0$ or $x - 8 = 0$
4. Solve each equation. $x = 0$ or $x = 8$
5. Check each solution. $2x^2 = 16x$

$$2 \cdot 0^2 \stackrel{?}{=} 16 \cdot 0 \text{ or } 2 \cdot 8^2 \stackrel{?}{=} 16 \cdot 8$$
$$0 = 0 \qquad\qquad 128 = 128$$

Example 4 Solve $x^2 - 50 = 5x$.

$$x^2 - 50 = 5x$$
$$x^2 - 5x - 50 = 0 \quad \textit{Subtract } 5x \textit{ from each side.}$$
$$(x - 10)(x + 5) = 0 \quad \textit{Factor the polynomial.}$$
$$x - 10 = 0 \quad \text{or} \quad x + 5 = 0$$
$$x = 10 \qquad\qquad x = -5$$

The two solutions are 10 and –5.

Solve each of the following.

1. $x^2 + 3x + 2 = 0$

2. $x^2 - 9 = 0$

3. $x^2 + x - 6 = 0$

4. $4x^2 = 8x$

5. $x^2 - 6x + 5 = 0$

6. $x^2 - 2x + 1 = 0$

7. $x^2 - 16 = 0$

8. $2x^2 = 50$

9. $x^2 + 10x + 21 = 0$

10. $x^2 + 4x = -4$

11. $6x^2 - 5x + 1 = 0$

12. $x^2 + 2x - 15 = 0$

13. $x^2 - 10x + 21 = 0$

14. $6x^2 + 5x + 1 = 0$

15. $8x^2 + 6x - 2 = 0$

16. $6x^2 - 5x = 1$

17. $8x^2 - 15x - 2 = 0$

18. $8x^2 + 8x + 2 = 0$

19. $12x^2 + x - 1 = 0$

20. $12x^2 + 12x - 9 = 0$

21. $-4x^2 = 32x + 48$

22. $x^2 + 2x + \frac{3}{4} = 0$

23. $2x^2 - \frac{2}{3}x - \frac{1}{6} = 0$

24. $1 = 3x^2 + 2x$

5.2 Completing the Square

Factoring the polynomials in equations such as $2x^2 + 16x - 418 = 0$ may be time-consuming. Recall the method used to solve equations such as $x^2 = 9$ and $y^2 = 625$. Study the method of **completing the square** shown in the following.

Example 1   Solve $2x^2 + 16x - 418 = 0$.

$$2x^2 + 16x - 418 = 0$$

$$2x^2 + 16x = 418 \qquad \textit{Add 418 to each side.}$$

$$x^2 + 8x = 209 \qquad \textit{Divide each side by 2.}$$

$$x^2 + 8x + 4^2 = 209 + 4^2 \qquad \textit{Add } \left(\tfrac{8}{2}\right)^2 \textit{ or } 4^2 \textit{ to each side.}$$

$$x^2 + 8x + 16 = 225$$

$$(x + 4)^2 = 225 \qquad \textit{Write } x^2 + 8x + 16 \textit{ is } (x + 4)^2.$$

$$x + 4 = \pm 15 \qquad \textit{Find the square root of each side.}$$

You now have two equations.   Solve each of them.

$$x + 4 = 15 \qquad x + 4 = -15$$
$$x = 11 \qquad x = -19$$

A check shows that the solutions are 11 and −19.

Notice that in the step in which $\left(\tfrac{8}{2}\right)^2$ was added to each side, the expression on the left became the square of the binomial $x + \tfrac{8}{2}$, or $x + 4$.

To solve a quadratic equation in standard form by the method of completing the square, use the following steps.

1. Add the opposite of the constant term to each side.
2. Divide each side by the coefficient of x^2.
3. Add to each side the square of half the coefficient of x.
4. Write the trinomial on the left as a binomial squared.
5. Find the square root of each side.
6. Solve each of the resulting equations.

Example 2   Solve $x^2 + 6x + 8 = 0$ by completing the square.

$$x^2 + 6x + 8 = 0$$

1. Add -8 to each side.

$$-8 + x^2 + 6x + 8 = -8$$

2. Division by 1 results in the same equation.

$$x^2 + 6x = -8$$

3. Add $\left(\tfrac{6}{2}\right)^2$ or 3^2 to each side.

$$x^2 + 6x + 3^2 = -8 + 3^2$$

4. Write the trinomial as a binomial squared.

$$x^2 + 6x + 9 = 1$$

5. Find the square root of each side.

$$x + 3 = \pm 1$$

6. Solve each of the resulting equations.

$$x + 3 = 1 \qquad x + 3 = -1$$
$$x = -2 \qquad x = -4$$

The solutions are −2 and −4. You can check this equation by solving it through factoring.

Example 3 Solve $x^2 - 4x - 3 = 0$ by completing the square.

$$x^2 - 4x - 3 = 0$$
$$x^2 - 4x = 3$$
$$x^2 - 4x + 4 = 3 + 4 \quad \text{Can you see why 4 is added?}$$
$$(x+2)^2 = 7$$
$$x + 2 = \pm\sqrt{7}$$

$$x + 2 = \sqrt{7} \qquad x + 2 = -\sqrt{7}$$
$$x = \sqrt{7} - 2 \qquad x = -\sqrt{7} - 2$$

The solutions may be written $-2 \pm \sqrt{7}$.

Example 4 Solve $9x^2 - 3x - 2 = 0$ by completing the square.

$$9x^2 - 3x - 2 = 0$$
$$9x^2 - 3x = 2$$
$$x^2 - \frac{1}{3}x = \frac{2}{9} \qquad \text{Divide each side by 9.}$$
$$x^2 - \frac{1}{3}x + \frac{1}{36} = \frac{2}{9} + \frac{1}{36} \quad \text{Note } \left[\frac{1}{2}\left(-\frac{1}{3}\right)\right]^2 = \left(-\frac{1}{6}\right)^2 \text{ or } \frac{1}{36}.$$
$$\left(x - \frac{1}{6}\right)^2 = \frac{1}{4} \qquad \text{Can you see that } \frac{2}{9} + \frac{1}{36} = \frac{1}{4}?$$
$$x - \frac{1}{6} = \pm\frac{1}{2}$$

$$x - \frac{1}{6} = \frac{1}{2} \qquad x - \frac{1}{6} = -\frac{1}{2}$$
$$x = \frac{1}{2} + \frac{1}{6} \qquad x = -\frac{1}{2} + \frac{1}{6}$$
$$x = \frac{2}{3} \qquad x = -\frac{1}{3}$$

A check shows that the solutions are $\frac{2}{3}$ and $-\frac{1}{3}$.

Solve each of the following by finding the square root of each side.

1. $x^2 = 49$ **2.** $y^2 = 289$ **3.** $w^2 = 5$

4. $(y-5)^2 = 100$ **5.** $x^2 + 12x + 36 = 16$ **6.** $(x+3)^2 = 25$

Find the number to add to each of the following to produce a trinomial equal to a binomial squared.

Sample: Add 64 to $x^2 - 16x$ to produce $(x-8)^2$.

7. $w^2 - 8w$ **8.** $y^2 - 14y$ **9.** $z^2 + 26z$

10. $x^2 + 8x$ **11.** $x^2 - 5x$ **12.** $x^2 + x$

Solve each of the following by completing the square.

13. $x^2 - 12x = 45$ **14.** $x^2 + 14x + 24 = 0$ **15.** $z^2 - 10z + 14 = 0$

16. $x^2 + 2x - 5 = 0$ **17.** $x^2 + 6x - 25 = 0$ **18.** $x^2 + 5x + 4 = 0$

19. $18x^2 + 9x + 1 = 0$ **20.** $4x^2 - 8x - 5 = 0$ **21.** $8x^2 - 2x - 1 = 0$

5.3 The Quadratic Formula

The following expresses a generalized equation.

$$ax^2 + bx + c = 0, \; a \neq 0$$

You can use the method of completing the square to solve any quadratic equation. Therefore, to find a formula for the solution for any quadratic equation, solve the generalized equation above by completing the square.

Example 1 Solve $ax^2 + bx + c = 0$ by completing the square.

$$ax^2 + bx + c = 0$$

$$ax^2 + bx = -c \qquad \textit{Add } -c \textit{ to both sides.}$$

$$\frac{ax^2}{a} + \frac{bx}{a} = \frac{-c}{a} \qquad \textit{Divide both sides by a.}$$

$$x^2 + \frac{bx}{a} + \frac{b^2}{4a^2} = \frac{-c}{a} + \frac{b^2}{4a^2} \qquad \textit{Add } \left(\frac{b}{2a}\right)^2 \textit{ or } \frac{b^2}{4a^2} \textit{ to both sides.}$$

$$\left(x + \frac{b}{2a}\right)^2 = \frac{-4ac + b^2}{4a^2} \qquad \textit{Simplify the equation.}$$

$$x + \frac{b}{2a} = \frac{\pm\sqrt{b^2 - 4ac}}{2a} \qquad \textit{Find the square root of both sides.}$$

$$x = \frac{-b + \sqrt{b^2 - 4ac}}{2a} \quad \text{or} \quad x = \frac{-b - \sqrt{b^2 - 4ac}}{2a}$$

The solutions of a quadratic equation of the form $ax^2 + bx + c = 0$, $a \neq 0$, are given by the formula

$$x = \frac{-b \pm \sqrt{b^2 - 4ac}}{2a}.$$

Example 2 Solve $x^2 - x - 6 = 0$ by using the quadratic formula.

$$x^2 - x - 6 = 0 \quad a = 1, \; b = -1, \; c = -6$$

$$x = \frac{-b \pm \sqrt{b^2 - 4ac}}{2a}$$

$$x = \frac{-(-1) \pm \sqrt{(-1)^2 - 4(1)(-6)}}{2(1)} \qquad \textit{Substitute for a, b, and c in the formula.}$$

$$x = \frac{1 \pm \sqrt{1 + 24}}{2} \text{ or } \frac{1 \pm \sqrt{25}}{2}$$

$$x = \frac{1 \pm 5}{2} \qquad \textit{Therefore, } x = 3 \textit{ or } x = -2.$$

Find a, b, and c for each of the following equations in the form $ax^2 + bx + c = 0$.

1. $x^2 - 2x - 15 = 0$ **2.** $x^2 + 5x + 4 = 0$ **3.** $x^2 - 24x - 35 = 0$

4. $\frac{1}{2}x^2 - x - 2 = 0$ **5.** $2x^2 - 9x - 5 = 0$ **6.** $3x^2 + x - 3 = 0$

7–12. Solve each of the equations in exercises **1–6** by using the quadratic formula.

5.4 Systems of Equations

Sometimes problems in algebra are solved using two variables, in a **system** of two equations. Suppose the sum of two numbers is 14 and their difference is 4. You can find the numbers by **solving a system** of equations simultaneously.

Define the variables. Let x = the greater number.
Let y = the lesser number.

Write the system of equations. The sum of the numbers   is 14.
  The first equation: $x + y$ $= 14$
                  The difference of the numbers   is 4.
   The second equation: $x - y$ $= 4.$

You can use two methods to solve the system of equations $x + y = 14$ and $x - y = 4$. The first method uses substitution.

Method 1 Solve the first equation for x.

$$x = 14 - y$$
$$(14 - y) - y = 4 \qquad \text{\textit{Substitute } } 14 - y \text{ \textit{for} } x \text{ \textit{in the}}$$
$$14 - 2y = 4 \qquad \text{\textit{second equation and solve for} } y.$$
$$-2y = -10$$
$$y = 5$$
$$x + 5 = 14 \qquad \text{\textit{To find} } x, \text{ \textit{substitute} } 5 \text{ \textit{for} } y \text{ \textit{in the}}$$
$$x = 9 \qquad \text{\textit{first equation. Solve for} } x.$$

The numbers are 9 and 5.

You know that adding the same number to each side of an equation produces another equation. The second method uses the idea that equal amounts added to both sides of an equation produce an equivalent equation.

Method 2 $x + y = 14$ *Add the two equations by first adding the left sides.*
$\underline{x - y = 4}$
$2x \quad = 18$ *Notice that the y terms are eliminated. Then, add the right sides.*
$x = 9$ *Solve the resulting equation for x.*
$9 + y = 14$ *Substitute 9 for x in the first equation and solve for y.*
$y = 5$

The solution of the system is written as the ordered pair (9, 5). Always name the solution for x first. You can use subtraction in the same way you used addition to eliminate a variable term.

Example 1 Solve the system $2x + 3y = 1$ and $2x - y = 5$ by elimination.
$2x + 3y = 1$
$\underline{-(2x - y = 5)}$
$4y = -4$ *Subtract on the left and right sides.*
    This time the x terms are eliminated.
$y = -1$ *Solve the resulting equation for y.*

$$2x-(-1)=5 \quad \text{Substitute } -1 \text{ for } y \text{ in the second equation.}$$
$$2x+1=5 \quad \text{Solve for } x.$$
$$2x=4$$
$$x=2 \quad \text{The solution of the system is } (2, -1).$$

In the system shown below at the left, to eliminate a variable term by addition or subtraction, you must first multiply the equation $x + 2y = 5$ by –2.

$x + 2y = 5$ Multiply by –2. ⟩ $-2x - 4y = -10$ Why was –2 chosen?
$2x + 3y = 6$ $\underline{2x + 3y = \quad 6}$ Now add.
$$-y = -4$$
$$y = 4$$
$$x + 2(4) = 5 \quad \text{Substitute 4 for } y \text{ in the first}$$
$$x + 8 = 5 \quad \text{equation and solve for } x.$$
$$x = -3 \quad \text{The solution is } (-3, 4).$$

Example 2 Use multiplication to solve the system of equations $3x - 2y = -1$ and $2x + 5y = 12$ by elimination.

$3x - 2y = -1$ Multiply by 2. ⟩ $6x - \quad 4y = \quad -2$ Note that the coefficients

$2x + 5y = 12$ Multiply by –3. ⟩ $\underline{-6x - 15y = -36}$ of the x terms are opposites
$$-19y = -38 \quad \text{The x term is eliminated}$$
$$y = 2$$
$$3x - 2(2) = -1$$
$$3x - 4 = -1$$
$$3x = 3$$
$$x = 1 \quad \text{The solution is } (1, \ 2).$$

Solve each of the following exercises for y.
1. $y + 3 = x$ 2. $y - 6 = 24$ 3. $-2x + y = 10$
4. $2y + x = 7$ 5. $-y = 2x + 1$ 6. $8x - 8y = 16$

Solve each system of equations by substitution.
7. $x - y = 3$ and $4x + 3y = 12$ 8. $x + y = 7$ and $2x - 3y = 9$
9. $y = x$ and $3x + 2y = 20$ 10. $y = 3x$ and $x + y = 2$

Solve each of the following systems by elimination.
11. $6x - 7y = 21$ and $3x + 7y = 6$ 12. $3x - 2y = 11$ and $x - 2y = 1$
13. $x + y = 3$ and $x - y = 13$ 14. $3x + y = 12$ and $x + y = 8$

State what number you would multiply each equation by in order to solve the system by elimination.
15. $2x + 5y = 8$ and $x + 3y = 3$ 16. $3x + 2y = 14$ and $x - y = 6$
17. $2x - 3y = 7$ and $3x + 7y = -1$ 18. $2x + 4y = 12$ and $x + y = 4$
19. $3x + 2y = -2$ and $15x + 6y = 12$ 20. $x - y = 6$ and $3x + 5y = 30$
21–26. Solve, by elimination, each system of equations in exercises 15–20.

Solve each of the following systems by substitution or elimination.
27. $2x - 3y = 18$ and $5x + 3y = 3$ 28. $2x + 2y = 8$ and $4x - 6y = 36$
29. $2x + 3y = 12$ and $x + y = 4$ 30. $2x + 4y = 16$ and $x + 3y = 5$

5.5 Systems of Equations in Problem Solving

Systems of equations are particularly suited for solving some kinds of problems. In some motion problems, such as the one in the following example, the current or wind adds to the rate of a body moving with it. It decreases the rate of the body moving against it.

Example 1   Eric rows upstream at 4 miles per hour and downstream at 6 miles per hour. Find Eric's rate in still water and the rate of the current.

Define variables.   Let x = Eric's rate in still water.
Let y = the rate of the current.

Write a system of equations.

Eric's rate in still water	less	the rate of the current	equals	Eric's rate upstream
x	$-$	y	$=$	4

Eric's rate in still water	plus	the rate of the current	equals	Eric's rate downstream
x	$+$	y	$=$	6

Solve the system of equations.

$$x - y = 4 \quad \text{Add to eliminate } y.$$
$$x + y = 6$$
$$2x = 10 \quad \text{Solve for } x.$$
$$x = 5$$
$$5 + y = 6 \quad \text{Substitute 5 for } x \text{ in the}$$
$$y = 1 \quad \text{second equation.}$$

Check the solution.   Eric's rate less the current is 5 − 1 or 4 mph, his rate upstream. His rate plus the current is 5 + 1 or 6 mph, the rate downstream.

Answer the problem.   Eric's rate in still water is 5 mph. The current's rate is 1 mph.

The mixture problem that follows in Example 2 is solved with two variables. A solution with one variable can be used to check the answer.

Example 2   Mr. Ramirez sells bluegrass seed for $3.50 per pound and a fescue seed for $1.70 per pound. He wishes to make a 50-pound mixture to sell for $2.96 per pound. Find how much of each kind of seed he must use in the mixture.

Define variables.   Let x = the number of pounds of bluegrass seed.
Let y = the number of pounds of fescue seed.

Write a system of equations.

The number of pounds of bluegrass seed	plus	the number of pounds of fescue seed	equals	the number of pounds of the mixture
x	$+$	y	$=$	50

The cost of x pounds of bluegrass seed	plus	the cost of y pounds of fescue seed	equals	the cost of 50 pounds of the mixture
$3.50x$	$+$	$1.70y$	$=$	$2.96(50)$

Solve the system of equations.

$$x + y = 50$$
$$3.50x + 1.70y = 2.96(50)$$

$-3.50x - 3.50y = -175$	*Multiply the first equation by –3.50.*
$\underline{3.50x + 1.70y = 148}$	*Add the equations.*
$-1.80y = -27$	*Solve for y.*
$y = 15$	
$x + 15 = 50$	*Substitute for 15 for y.*
$x = 35$	*Solve for x.*

Answer the problem.   Mr. Ramirez mixes 35 pounds of bluegrass seed with 15 pounds of fescue seed.

For each problem, define two variables. Then write and solve a system of equations.

1. Candy worth \$3.55 per pound is mixed with candy worth \$4.30 per pound. How much of each kind must be used to have 30 pounds of a mixture worth \$4.05 per pound?

2. The Cheery Coffee Company mixed two kinds of coffee. One kind costs \$4.00 per pound and the other costs \$4.75 per pound. They want 100 pounds worth \$4.30 per pound. How much of each kind should they use?

3. David bought 3 hamburgers and 2 servings of french fries at Diane's Drive-up for \$6.25. If a serving of fries costs 25¢ more than a hamburger, what is the cost of each?

4. The Georgia Tea Company mixes two kinds of tea. One kind costs \$4.00 per pound and the other costs \$3.00 per pound. They want 40 pounds worth \$3.375 per pound. How much of each kind should they use?

5. Mr. Carlson took 2.5 hours to fly his airplane a distance of 360 miles against a steady wind. It took him 2 hours to make the return trip with the wind. Find Mr. Carlson's rate in calm air, and the rate of the wind. Use $r = \dfrac{d}{t}$.

6. Two people start driving toward each other on the same highway at the same time from towns 420 miles apart. One car travels 15 miles per hour faster than the other. What is the rate of each car if they meet in 4 hours?

7. A boat took 1 hour and 50 minutes to go 55 km downstream and 3 hours, 40 minutes to return. Find the boat's rate in still water and the rate of the current.

8. An art store sells brushes for \$1.80 each and tubes of paint for \$2.20 each. Sandra spent \$1.20 more on brushes than on paint. She spent a total of \$27.60. How many brushes and tubes of paint did she buy?

9. A plane took 1 hour and 20 minutes to go 600 miles when flying with the jet stream and 2 hours 40 minutes to fly the same distance against it. Find the plane's rate in calm air and the rate of the jet stream.

10. Leslie buys 38 stamps for \$9.88. If each stamp cost either 32¢ or 20¢, how many of each kind did she buy?

CHAPTER FIVE   SOLUTIONS and ANSWERS

Secton 5.1

1. $x = -2$ or -1
2. $x = \pm 3$
3. $x = -3$ or 2
4. $x = 0$ or 2
5. $x = 1$ or 5
6. $x = 1$
7. $x = \pm 4$
8. $x = \pm 5$
9. $x = -7$ or -3
10. $x = -2$
11. $x = \frac{1}{3}$ or $\frac{1}{2}$
12. $x = -5$ or 3
13. $x = 3$ or 7
14. $x = -\frac{1}{2}$ or $-\frac{1}{3}$
15. $x = -1$ or $\frac{1}{4}$
16. $x = -\frac{1}{6}$ or 1
17. $x = -\frac{1}{8}$ or 2
18. $x = -\frac{1}{2}$
19. $x = -\frac{1}{3}$ or $\frac{1}{4}$
20. $x = -\frac{3}{2}$ or $\frac{1}{2}$
21. $x = -6$ or -2
22. $x = -\frac{3}{2}$ or $-\frac{1}{2}$
23. $x = -\frac{1}{6}$ or $\frac{1}{2}$
24. $x = -1$ or $\frac{1}{3}$

Section 5.2

1. $x^2 = 49$
   $x = \pm 7$

2. $y^2 = 289$
   $y = \pm 17$

3. $w^2 = 5$
   $w = \pm \sqrt{5}$

4. $(y-5)^2 = 100$
   $y - 5 = \pm 10$
   $y - 5 + 5 = \pm 10 + 5$
   $y = -5$ or 15

5. $x^2 + 12x + 36 = 16$
   $(x+6)^2 = 16$
   $x + 6 = \pm 4$
   $x + 6 - 6 = \pm 4 - 6$
   $x = -10$ or -2

6. $(x+3)^2 = 25$
   $x + 3 = \pm 5$
   $x + 3 - 3 = \pm 5 - 3$
   $x = 2$ or -8

7. $w^2 - 8w$
   $\left(-\frac{8}{2}\right)^2 = 16$
   $w^2 - 8w + \underline{16} = (w-4)^2$

8. $y^2 - 14y$
   $\left(-\frac{14}{2}\right)^2 = \frac{196}{4} = 49$
   $y^2 - 14y + \underline{49} = (y-7)^2$

9. $z^2 + 26z$
   $\left(\frac{26}{2}\right)^2 = 169$
   $z^2 + 26z + \underline{169} = (z+13)^2$

10. $x^2 + 8x$
    $\left(\frac{8}{2}\right)^2 = 16$
    $x^2 + 0x + \underline{16} = (x+4)^2$

11. $x^2 - 5x + \frac{25}{4} = \left(x - \frac{5}{2}\right)^2$

12. $x^2 + x + \frac{1}{4} = \left(x + \frac{1}{2}\right)^2$

13. $x^2 - 12x = 45$
    $x^2 - 12x + 36 = 81$
    $(x-6)^2 = 81$
    $x - 6 = \pm 9$
    $x = \pm 9 + 6$
    $x = 15$ or -3

14. $x^2 + 14x + 24 = 0$
    $x^2 + 14x = -24$
    $x^2 + 14x + 49 = 25$
    $(x+7)^2 = 25$
    $x + 7 = \pm 5$
    $x = -7 \pm 5$
    $x = -2$ or -12

15. $z = 5 \pm \sqrt{11}$
16. $x = -1 \pm \sqrt{6}$
17. $x = -3 \pm \sqrt{34}$
18. $x = -1$ or -4
19. $x = -\frac{1}{3}$ or $-\frac{1}{6}$
20. $x = -\frac{1}{2}$ or $\frac{5}{2}$
21. $x = \frac{1}{2}$ or $-\frac{1}{4}$

Section 5.3

1. $x^2 - 2x - 15 = 0$
   $A = 1, B = -2, C = -15$

2. $x^2 + 5x + 4 = 0$
   $A = 1, B = 5, C = 4$

3. $x^2 - 24x - 35 = 0$
   $A = 1, B = -24, C = -35$

4. $\frac{1}{2}x^2 - x - 2 = 0$
   $A = \frac{1}{2}, B = -1, C = -2$

5. $2x^2 - 9x - 5 = 0$
   $A = 2, B = -9, C = -5$

6. $3x^2 + x - 3 = 0$
   $A = 3, B = 1, C = -3$

71

7.

$x^2 - 2x - 15 = 0$

$x = \dfrac{2 \pm \sqrt{4 - 4 \cdot 1(-15)}}{2 \cdot 1}$

$x = \dfrac{2 \pm \sqrt{64}}{2}$

$x = \dfrac{2 \pm 8}{2}$

$x = 1 \pm 4$

$x = 5 \text{ or } -3$

8.

$x^2 + 5x + 4 = 0$

$x = \dfrac{-5 \pm \sqrt{25 - 4 \cdot 1 \cdot 4}}{2 \cdot 1}$

$x = \dfrac{-5 \pm \sqrt{9}}{2}$

$x = -\dfrac{5}{2} \pm \dfrac{3}{2}$

$x = -1 \text{ or } -4$

9.

$x = 12 \pm \sqrt{179}$

10. $x = 1 \pm \sqrt{5}$

11. $x = -\dfrac{1}{2} \text{ or } 5$

12. $x = \dfrac{-1 \pm \sqrt{37}}{6}$

Section 5.4

1.
$y + 3 = x$
$\quad y = x - 3$

2.
$y - 6 = 24$
$\quad y = 30$

3.
$-2x + y = 10$
$\quad y = 10 + 2x$

4.
$2y + x = 7$
$2y = 7 - x$
$\quad y = \dfrac{7 - x}{2}$

5.
$-y = 2x + 1$
$\quad y = -2x - 1$

6.
$8x - 8y = 16$
$\quad -8y = 16 - 8x$
$\quad\quad y = -2 + x \text{ or } x - 2$

7.
$x - y = 3, \ 4x + 3y = 12$
$\quad x = 3 + y$
$\quad 4(3 + y) + 3y = 12$
$\quad 12 + 4y + 3y = 12$
$\quad\quad\quad\quad 7y = 0$
$\quad\quad\quad\quad\ y = 0$
$\quad x = 3 + 0$
$\quad x = 3$
Solution: (3, 0)

8.
$x + y = 7, \ 2x - 3y = 9$
$\quad x = 7 - y$
$\quad 2(7 - y) - 3y = 9$
$\quad 14 - 2y - 3y = 9$
$\quad\quad\ 14 - 5y = 9$
$\quad\quad\quad\ -5y = -5$
$\quad\quad\quad\quad\ y = 1$
$\quad x = 7 - 1$
$\quad x = 6$
Solution: (6, 1)

9. (4, 4) **10.** $\left(\dfrac{1}{2}, \dfrac{3}{2}\right)$ **11.** $\left(3, -\dfrac{3}{7}\right)$ **12.** (5, 2) **13.** (8, –5) **14.** (2, 6)

15.
$2x + 5y = 8$
$\quad x + 3y = 3$
Multiply $(x + 3y = 3)$ by -2

16.
$3x + 2y = 14$
$\quad x - y = 6$
Multiply $(x - y = 6)$ by 2

17.
Multiply $(2x - 3y = 7)$ by 3
Multiply $(3x + 7y = -1)$ by -2

18.
Multiply $(x + y = 4)$ by -2

19.
$3x + 2y = -2$
$15x + 6y = 12$
Multiply $(3x + 2y = -2)$ by -5 or by -3

20.
$x - y = 6$
$3x + 5y = 30$
Multiply $(x - y = 6)$ by -3

21.
$\begin{array}{ll} 2x + 5y = 8 & 2x + 5y = 8 \\ \underline{\ x + 3y = 3\ } & \underline{-2x - 6y = -6} \\ & \quad\ -y = 2 \\ & \quad\ \ y = -2 \end{array}$

$x + 3 \cdot -2 = 3$
$\quad x - 6 = 3$
$\quad\quad\ x = 9$
Solution: (9, –2)

22.
$\begin{array}{ll} 3x + 2y = 14 & 3x + 2y = 14 \\ \ x - y = 6 & \underline{2x - 2y = 12} \\ & \quad 5x = 26 \\ & \quad\ x = \dfrac{26}{5} \text{ or } 5\dfrac{1}{5} \end{array}$

$5\dfrac{1}{5} - y = 6$
$\quad\quad -y = \dfrac{4}{5}$
$\quad\quad\quad y = -\dfrac{4}{5}$

Solution: $\left(5\dfrac{1}{5}, -\dfrac{4}{5}\right)$

23. (2, –1) **24.** (2, 2) **25.** $\left(3, -\dfrac{11}{2}\right)$ **26.** $\left(7\dfrac{1}{2}, 1\dfrac{1}{2}\right)$ **27.** (3, –4)

28. (6, –2) **29.** (0, 4) **30.** (14, –3)

Section 5.5

1. Let x = the number of pounds of candy at $3.55 per pound.
   Let y = the number of pounds of candy at $4.30 per pound.

$$x + y = 30$$
$$3.55x + 4.30y = 4.05(30)$$

$x = 30 - y$	$-4.30x - 4.30y = -129.0$
$3.55(30 - y) + 4.30y = 4.05(30)$	$3.55x + 4.30y = 121.50$
$106.50 - 3.55y + 4.30y = 121.50$	$-0.75x = -7.50$
$0.75y = 15$	$x = 10$
$y = 20$	$x + y = 30$
$x + y = 30$	$y = 20$
$x + 20 = 30$	
$x = 10$	

   10 pounds of $3.55 per pound candy must be mixed with 20 pounds of $4.30 per pound candy to get 30 pounds of candy to sell at $4.05 per pound.

2. Let x = the number of pounds of coffee at $4.00 per pound.
   Let y = the number of pounds of coffee at $4.75 per pound.

$$x + y = 100$$
$$4.00x + 4.75y = 4.30(100)$$

$x = 100 - y$	$-4.00x - 4.00y = -400$
$4.00(100 - y) + 4.75y = 430$	$4.00x + 4.75y = 430$
$400 - 4y + 4.75y = 430$	$.75y = 30$
$.75y = 30$	$y = 40$
$y = 40$	$x + 40 = 100$
$x + 40 = 100$	$x = 60$
$x = 60$	

   Cheery Coffee Company needs to mix 60 pounds of $4.00 per pound coffee and 40 pounds of $4.75 per pound coffee to get 100 pounds of coffee to sell at $4.30 per pound.

3. The hamburgers at Diane's cost $1.15; the fries cost $1.40.

4. The Georgia Tea Company must mix 15 pounds of $4.00 per pound tea with 25 pounds of $3.00 per pound tea to get 40 pounds of tea selling at $3.375 per pound.

5. Mr. Carlson flies 162 miles per hour in calm air; the wind is blowing at a rate of 18 miles per hour.

6. The first car travels at 60 mph; the second car travels at 45 mph.

7. The rate of the boat in still water is $22\frac{1}{2}$ miles per hour; the rate of the current is $7\frac{1}{2}$ miles per hour.

8. Sandra bought 8 brushes and 6 tubes of paint.

9. The plane flies 337.5 miles per hour in calm air. The rate of the jet stream is 112.5 miles per hour.

10. Leslie bought nineteen 32¢ stamps and nineteen 20¢ stamps.

CHAPTER 6   INTRODUCTION TO GEOMETRY

6.1 Angles

An exact location in space suggests the idea of a **point** in geometry. Points have no size. They are represented in drawings by dots and are named by capital letters.

A **line** may be thought of as a straight path extending in both directions indefinitely. A line is represented by double arrows as shown at the right. A line is named by a lower case letter, such as line ℓ or by naming two points on the line, such in as $\overleftrightarrow{AB}$ read *line AB*.

A never ending straight path in one direction suggests a **ray**. A ray includes a point called the **endpoint** and all the points on the line on one side of that endpoint. In the drawing above, $\overrightarrow{AB}$, read *ray AB*, includes endpoint A and the points $\overleftrightarrow{AB}$ on the same side as B. The point named first always is the endpoint of the ray. Thus, $\overrightarrow{AB}$ and $\overrightarrow{BA}$ are different rays.

An **angle** is formed by two different rays that have a common endpoint called the **vertex** of the angle. The angle shown at the right is named $\angle ABC$, read *angle ABC*. Notice the middle letter of the name is the vertex. An angle also may be named by its vertex, such as $\angle B$ in this case.

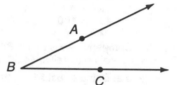

B is the vertex.
$\overrightarrow{BC}$ is the initial side.
$\overrightarrow{BA}$ is the terminal side.

You can think of one ray of an angle, called the **initial side**, as fixed. Then, think that the other ray, the **terminal side**, as rotated about the vertex. The measurement of the rotation usually is given in **degrees**. If a complete rotation is separated into 360 equal parts, each part is an angle of 1°. Thus, the measurement of a complete rotation is 360°.

Each degree also is separated into 60 equal parts called **minutes**. Furthermore, one minute is separated into 60 **seconds**.

| 1 degree equals 60 minutes. | 1° = 60' |
| 1 minute equals 60 seconds. | 1' = 60" |

Angles are classified according to their measurements.

Type of Angle	Acute	Right	Obtuse	Straight	Reflex
Measurement of Angle	less than 90°	90°	between 90° and 180°	180°	greater than 180°
Picture					

In a drawing, the symbol ⌐ at a vertex means the angle formed is a right angle. The rays are **perpendicular** to each other at the vertex of a right angle. The symbol for the degree measure of $\angle ABC$ is $m\angle ABC$. If $\angle PQR$ is a right angle, then $m\angle PQR = 90$.

A protractor may be used to find the degree measure of an angle. Place the center of the protractor at the vertex of the angle. Use the scale that begins at 0 along one ray of the angle. The number of degrees is found where the other ray intersects the protractor.

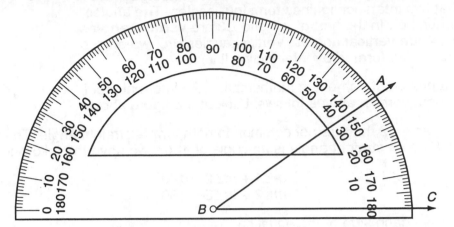

The degree measure of angle *ABC* is 35, m∠*ABC* = 35.

Use the figure below to answer exercise 1–7. Write yes or no.

1. $\overrightarrow{DG}$ and $\overrightarrow{DA}$ have the same endpoint.

2. $\overleftrightarrow{FG}$ and $\overleftrightarrow{CF}$ name the same line.

3. ∠*AGD* is a straight angle.

4. $\overrightarrow{GA}$ and $\overrightarrow{AG}$ name the same ray.

5. ∠*CGD* is obtuse.

6. Two angles of the figure are named ∠*AGB*. One is acute and the other is reflex.

7. *B* is a point of $\overleftrightarrow{GC}$.

Use the figure below to find the measurement of each of the following. Then classify the angle as acute, right, obtuse, or straight.

8. ∠*RVZ*
9. ∠*TVZ*
10. ∠*WVZ*
11. ∠*YVZ*
12. ∠*QVP*
13. ∠*SVZ*
14. ∠*QVZ*
15. ∠*SVP*
16. ∠*YVP*
17. ∠*XVZ*
18. ∠*TVP*
19. ∠*WVP*

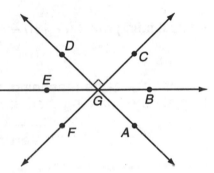

Find the measurement of the angle that corresponds to each of the following parts of a complete rotation of 360°.

20. $\frac{3}{4}$
21. $\frac{1}{4}$
22. $\frac{1}{8}$
23. 12.5%
24. $\frac{4}{9}$

What part of a complete rotation is an angle having the following measurements?

25. 60°
26. 40°
27. 180°
28. *x*°
29. 279°

75

6.2 Pairs of Angles

Two lines **intersect** if they have a point in common. The figure at the right shows that two intersecting lines form four angles. The angles are named by number. In the figure, ∠1 and ∠3 are **vertical angles**. Also, ∠2 and ∠4 are vertical angles. Vertical angles are two angles without common sides formed by intersecting lines.

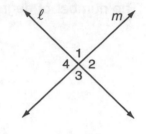

A **theorem** is a proved statement in mathematics. An informal proof of a theorem about vertical angles follows. Look at the figure above.

The sides of ∠1 and ∠2 that are not common to both form a straight angle. The same is true of ∠2 and ∠3. Since a straight angle is an angle of 180°, we have the following equations.

$$m\angle 1 + m\angle 2 = 180$$
$$m\angle 2 + m\angle 3 = 180$$

Subtract $m\angle 2$ from each side of the equation.

$$m\angle 1 = 180 - m\angle 2$$
$$m\angle 3 = 180 - m\angle 2$$

By substituting $m\angle 3$ for $180 - m\angle 2$ in the first equation, we have the following.

$$m\angle 1 = m\angle 3$$

Following the same reasoning, you can show that $m\angle 2 = m\angle 4$. From these conclusions, you can state the following theorem in general.

> **Vertical angles have the same measure.**

Example 1 Find the measurement of each angle in the figure below.

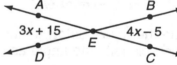

∠AED and ∠BEC are vertical angles.
Their measures are the same.
$m\angle AED = m\angle BEC$
$3x + 15 = 4x - 5$ *Solve for x.*
$15 + 5 = 4x - 3x$
$20 = x$
$3x + 15 = 3(20) + 15$ *Substitute 20 for x in 3x + 15.*
       $= 75$ $m\angle AED = m\angle BEC = 75$.
∠AED and ∠DEC form a straight angle.
$m\angle AED + m\angle DEC = 180$
    $75 + m\angle DEC = 180$ *Solve for m∠DEC.*
        $m\angle DEC = 180 - 75$
             $= 105$

∠DEC and ∠AEB are vertical angles with the same measure.
Thus, $m\angle AEB = 105$.
The measurements of ∠AED and ∠BEC are each 75°.
The measurements of ∠DEC and ∠AEB are each 105°.

Two angles can be related by the sum of their measures.
Two angles are **supplementary** if and only if the sum of their degree measure is 180.
The angles shown at the right are supplementary.
In the figure showing vertical angles, ∠1 and ∠2 are
supplementary, as are ∠2 and ∠3. Also, ∠4 is the
supplement of ∠1, and ∠3 is the supplement of ∠4.

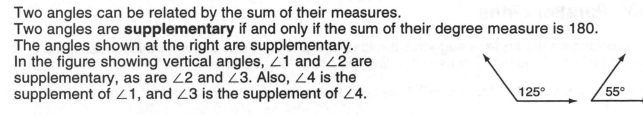

Example 2   Find the measurement of the supplement of an angle of 48°3'.
Since there are 60' in 1°, then 179°60' = 180°.
Subtract 48°3' from 179°60'.
179°60'
−48° 3'
131°57'
The measurement of the supplementary angle of 48°3' is 131°57'.

Two angles are **complementary** if and only if the sum of their degree measures is 90.
The figure below shows two pairs that complement each other.

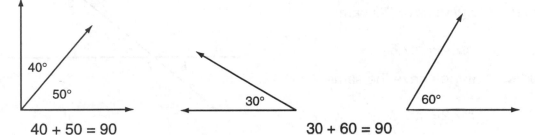

40 + 50 = 90   30 + 60 = 90

Angles A and B are supplementary. Find m∠A when the degree measure of ∠B is as follows.

1. 70°   2. 45°   3. 130°   4. 77°

5. 110.5°   6. $12\frac{1}{3}°$ 7. 3.07°   8. $x°$

*Angles M and P are complementary. Find the measurement of ∠M for each of the following
measurements of ∠P.*

9. 65°   10. 38°   11. 71°29'   12. 16°1'

13. 42°32'10"   14. 66°21'38"   15. 1°41'7"   16. $r°$

Find the value of x in each of the following.

17.   18.   19.   20.

21.   22.   23.   24.

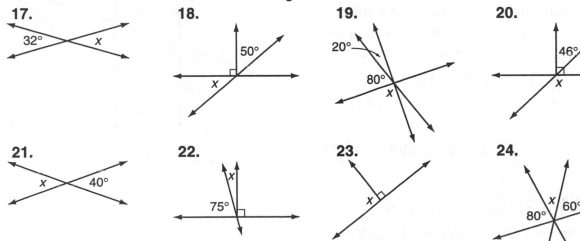

6.3   Parallel Lines

A never-ending flat surface suggests the idea of a **plane**. A plane has no thickness. A line is said to lie in a plane if all points of the line are points of the plane.

Two lines are **parallel** if and only if they lie in the same plane and do not intersect.

Look at the figure below. Line ℓ is parallel to line n. This may be written line line $\ell\|$line n. A line that intersects a pair of lines is called a **transversal**. Line t is a transversal that intersects lines ℓ and n. When parallel lines are intersected by a transversal, pairs of angles with the same measure are formed. These angle pairs have special names as indicated in the following.

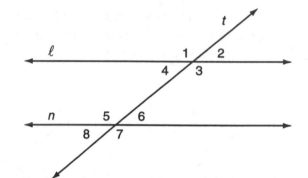

Corresponding angles have the same measure.

$m\angle 1 = m\angle 5 \qquad m\angle 2 = m\angle 6$
$m\angle 3 = m\angle 7 \qquad m\angle 4 = m\angle 8$

Alternate interior angles have the same measure.

$m\angle 3 = m\angle 5 \qquad m\angle 4 = m\angle 6$

Alternate exterior angles have the same measure.

$m\angle 1 = m\angle 7 \qquad m\angle 2 = m\angle 8$

Furthermore, **consecutive interior angles** are supplementary.

$m\angle 3 + m\angle 6 = 180 \quad m\angle 4 + m\angle 5 = 180$

Use the figure at the right to answer each of the following.
$\overleftrightarrow{AB}\|\overleftrightarrow{CD}$ and $\overleftrightarrow{EF}$ is a transversal intersecting $\overleftrightarrow{AB}$ and $\overleftrightarrow{CD}$.

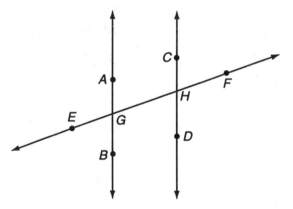

1. Name two pairs of alternate interior angles.

2. Name two pairs of consecutive interior angles.

3. Name four pairs of corresponding angles.

4. Name two pairs of alternate exterior angles.

5. Suppose $m\angle AGH = 70$. Find $m\angle CHF$.

6. Name four pairs of vertical angles.

7. If $m\angle CHF = 30 + x$ and $m\angle EGB = 2x - 15$, find x.

8. If $m\angle BGH = \dfrac{x}{2} + 22$ and $m\angle DHG = \dfrac{2x - 2}{5}$, find $m\angle BGH$.

9. Suppose $m\angle EGB = 2x + 5$ and $m\angle CHG = 3x + 25$. Find $m\angle CHF$.

10. Suppose $m\angle CHG = 100$. Find $m\angle BGH$.

6.4 Triangles

A line **segment** consists of two endpoints and the points of the line between them. Segments are named by their endpoints.

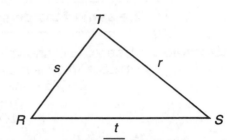

In the figure shown at the right, three segments named $\overline{RS}$, $\overline{ST}$, and $\overline{TR}$ form a **triangle**. Each segment is a **side** of the triangle. Two sides intersect in a common endpoint, or **vertex**, forming an angle of the triangle.

Triangles are named by their vertices. Thus, the triangle shown at right is named $\triangle RST$, read, *triangle RST*.

The measure of $\overline{ST}$ is usually symbolized ST. Notice that triangles are sometimes labeled so that r is the measure of the side opposite $\angle R$.

Triangles can be classified by the number of sides with the same measure. In a drawing, segments with the same number of marks have the same measure.

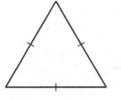

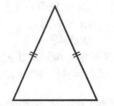

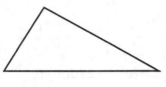

An **equilateral** triangle has three sides with the same measure.

An **isosceles** triangle has two sides with the same measure.

A **scalene** triangle has no sides with the same measure.

Triangles can be classified by their angles. All triangles have at least two acute angles. Use the third angle to classify the triangle.

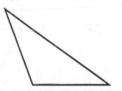

A **right** triangle has one right angle.

An **obtuse** triangle has one obtuse angle.

An **acute** triangle has three acute angles.

Look at $\triangle ABC$ shown at the right. Suppose $\overleftrightarrow{DE}$ is drawn parallel to $\overline{AC}$. Then $\overline{AB}$ and $\overline{BC}$ are transversals that intersect $\overleftrightarrow{DE}$ and $\overline{AC}$. Thus, $\angle 1$ and $\angle 5$ are alternate interior angles. Another pair of alternate interior angles are $\angle 3$ and $\angle 4$.

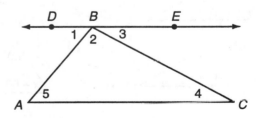

Further, $m\angle 1 = m\angle 5$ and $m\angle 3 = m\angle 4$, since alternate interior angles have the same measure.

Since $\angle 1$, $\angle 2$, and $\angle 3$ form a straight angle, $m\angle 1 + m\angle 2 + m\angle 3 = 180$. Substitute $m\angle 5$ for $m\angle 1$ and $m\angle 4$ for $m\angle 3$.

$$m\angle 5 + m\angle 2 + m\angle 4 = 180$$

The following theorem has been informally proven.

> **The sum of the degree measures of the angles of a triangle is 180.**

Example 1 Use $\triangle ABC$ shown on page 80. Suppose $m\angle 2 = 75$ and $m\angle 5 = 42$. Find $m\angle 4$.

$$m\angle 5 + m\angle 2 + m\angle 4 = 180$$
$$42 + 75 + m\angle 4 = 180$$
$$m\angle 4 = 180 - (42 + 75)$$
$$m\angle 4 = 63$$

Example 2 In $\triangle KLM$, $m\angle K$ is two times $m\angle L$ and $m\angle L$ is four more than $m\angle M$. Find $m\angle K$, $m\angle L$, and $m\angle M$.

Define a variable	Let $x = m\angle M$.
	Let $x + 4 = m\angle L$ and $2(x + 4) = m\angle K$.
	$m\angle M + m\angle L + m\angle K = 180$
Write an equation.	$x + x + 4 + 2(x + 4) = 180$
Solve the equation.	$x + x + 4 + 2x + 8 = 180$
	$\qquad\qquad 4x = 180 - 12$
	$\qquad\qquad 4x = 168$
	$\qquad\qquad x = 42$
	$x + 4 = 46$ and $2(x + 4) = 92$
Answer the problem.	$m\angle K = 92$, $m\angle L = 46$, and $m\angle M = 42$.

Classify each triangle by its sides and then by its angles.

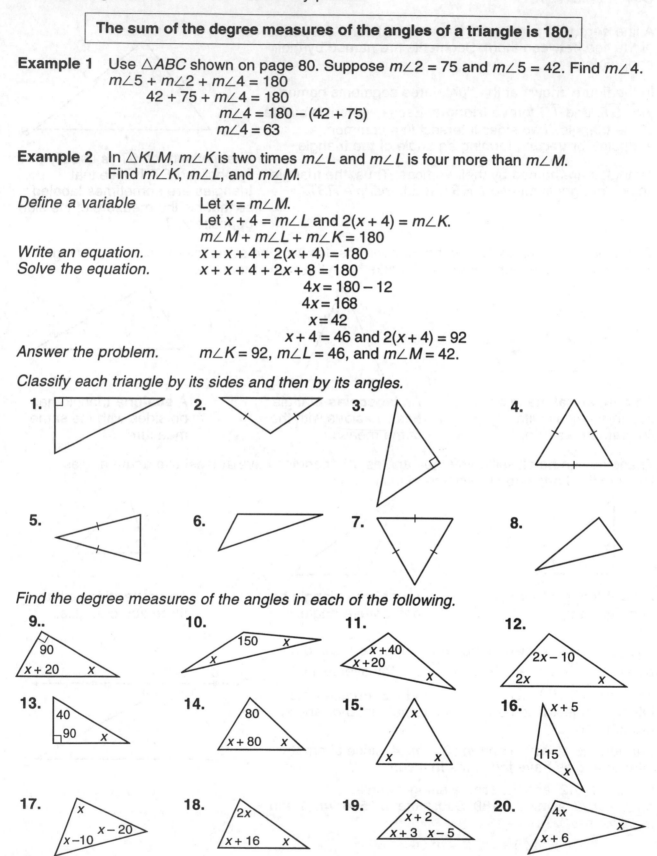

1.

2.

3.

4.

5.

6.

7.

8.

Find the degree measures of the angles in each of the following.

9. 90, $x + 20$, x

10. 150, x, x

11. $x + 40$, $x + 20$, x

12. $2x - 10$, $2x$, x

13. 40, 90, x

14. 80, $x + 80$, x

15. x, x, x

16. $x + 5$, 115, x

17. x, $x - 10$, $x - 20$

18. $2x$, $x + 16$, x

19. $x + 2$, $x + 3$, $x - 5$

20. $4x$, $x + 6$, x

6.5 Similar Triangles

Similar figures have the same shape but not necessarily the same size.
Similar triangles are shown below.

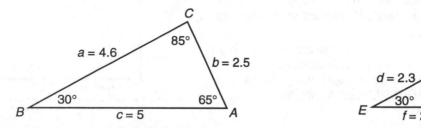

We write $\triangle ABC \sim \triangle DEF$. The symbol $\sim$ means *is similar to*. The vertices **correspond** in the order in which they are named. It would *not* be correct to write $\triangle ABC \sim \triangle DFE$.
Compare the measures of the corresponding angles.

$$m\angle A = m\angle D = 65 \qquad m\angle B = m\angle E = 30 \qquad m\angle C = m\angle F = 85$$

The sides opposite corresponding angles are called **corresponding sides**.
Compare the measures of corresponding sides.

$$\frac{a}{d} = \frac{4.6}{2.3} = 2 \qquad \frac{b}{e} = \frac{2.5}{1.25} = 2 \qquad \frac{c}{f} = \frac{5}{2.5} = 2$$

Since the ratios are the same, $\frac{a}{d} = \frac{b}{e} = \frac{c}{f}$.

The properties of corresponding parts of $\triangle ABC$ and $\triangle DEF$ are true for all similar triangles.

**The measures of corresponding angles of similar triangles are the same.
The measures of corresponding sides of similar triangles are in proportion.**

Example 1 In the diagram below, $\triangle JKL \sim \triangle RST$. Find r.

Write a proportion using the measures of corresponding sides.

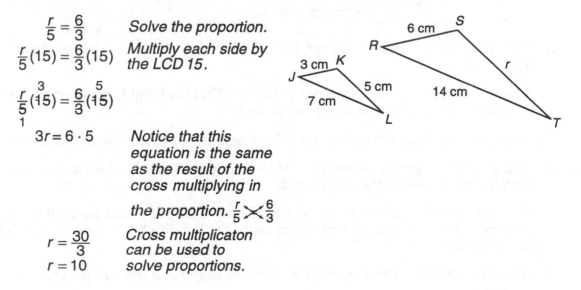

$\dfrac{r}{5} = \dfrac{6}{3}$ *Solve the proportion.*

$\dfrac{r}{5}(15) = \dfrac{6}{3}(15)$ *Multiply each side by the LCD 15.*

$\dfrac{r}{\underset{1}{5}}(\overset{3}{15}) = \dfrac{6}{3}(\overset{5}{15})$

$3r = 6 \cdot 5$ *Notice that this equation is the same as the result of the cross multiplying in the proportion. $\dfrac{r}{5}\!\!\times\!\!\dfrac{6}{3}$*

$r = \dfrac{30}{3}$ *Cross multiplicaton can be used to solve proportions.*

$r = 10$

You can be certain two triangles are similar if you know that two angles of one triangle have the same measure as two angles of the other triangle.

Example 2 Find the width of the river shown in the diagram.

The triangles are similar. Why? The sides opposite the vertical angles in the triangles correspond.

$$\frac{x}{36} = \frac{100}{60}$$ *Write a proportion using the measures of corresponding sides.*

$60x = 36(100)$ *Cross multiply.*

$$x = \frac{3600}{60}$$

$x = 60$ The river is 60 ft wide.

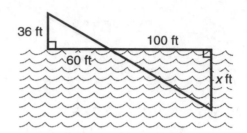

Example 3 Find the height of the flagpole at the right.

Vertical objects and their shadows form similar triangles. Why?

$$\frac{6}{x} = \frac{4}{18}$$

$4x = 6(18)$

$$x = \frac{108}{4}$$

$x = 27$ The flagpole is 27 ft high.

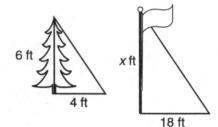

Name the corresponding sides and angles for each pair of similar triangles.

1.

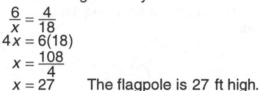

2.

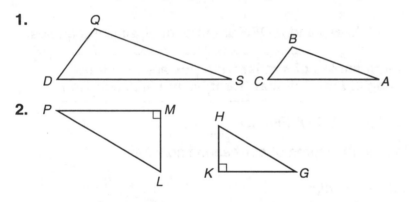

3. Triangle *ABC* is similar to triangle *DEF*. Suppose $a = 3$, $b = 6$, $c = 7$, and $d = 4$. Find *e* and *f*.

4. A meter stick casts a shadow that is 150 cm. Find the height of a building whose shadow is 6000 cm in length. (one meter = 100 cm)

5. Triangle *ABC* is similar to triangle *DEF*. Name the corresponding angles and sides.

6. Triangle *RST* is similar to triangle *JKL*. Suppose $r = 3$, $s = 15$, $t = 14$, and $j = 5$. Find the measures of the other sides.

7. A 10-foot ladder touches the side of a building at a point 8 feet above the ground. At what height would a 25-foot ladder touch the building if it makes the same angle with the ground?

8. A yardstick casts a shadow of 84 in. Find the height of a tree whose shadow is 560 in. in length.

82

6.6 The Pythagorean Theorem

In a right triangle, the two perpendicular sides are called the **legs** and the side opposite the right angle is called the **hypotenuse** of the triangle. As early as the sixth century B.C. a relationship was known between the measures of the legs and hypotenuse of every right triangle. This relationship is stated in a theorem traditionally associated with Pythagoras, a Greek mathematician. The Pythagorean Theorem follows.

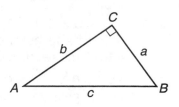

> **In a right triangle, if *a* and *b* represent the measures of the legs and *c* represents the measure of the hypotenuse, then $a^2 + b^2 = c^2$.**

You can use the Pythagorean Theorem to find the length of the side of a right triangle if you know the lengths of the other two sides.

Example 1 Suppose the lengths of the legs of a right triangle *ABC* are 9 cm and 12 cm. Find the length of the hypotenuse.

$$a^2 + b^2 = c^2 \quad \textit{Use the Pythagorean Theorem.}$$
$$9^2 + 12^2 = c^2 \quad \textit{Substitute 9 for a and 12 for b.}$$
$$81 + 144 = c^2 \quad \textit{Solve for c.}$$
$$225 = c^2$$
$$\pm\sqrt{225} = c$$
$$\pm 15 = c \quad \textit{Since length cannot be negative, reject } -15$$
$$\textit{as an answer for the problem.}$$

The length of the hypotenuse is 15 cm.

Example 2 A 13-foot ladder is placed against a house so that the foot of the ladder is five feet from the house. How far above the ground does the ladder touch the wall?

The ladder, wall, and ground from a right triangle. The ladder is on the hypotenuse. Let $c = 13$ and $a = 5$.

$$a^2 + b^2 = c^2$$
$$5^2 + b^2 = 13^2$$
$$b^2 = 169 - 25$$
$$b^2 = 144$$
$$b = \pm 12 \qquad \textit{Reject } -12.$$

The ladder touches the wall 12 feet from the ground.

Example 3 Determine whether the following could be the measures of the sides of a right triangle.

$a = 5, b = 7, c = 9.$

If the numbers are the measures of the sides of a right triangle, then an equation will result when they are substituted in the Pythagorean Theorem formula.

$a^2 + b^2 = c^2$

$5^2 + 7^2 \stackrel{?}{=} 9^2$ *Substitute the numbers in the Pythagorean formula.*

$25 + 49 \stackrel{?}{=} 81$

74 is not equal to 81. Therefore, the numbers are not the measures of the sides of a right triangle.

Find the values of a, b, or c.

1. $8^2 + 15^2 = c^2$

2. $6^2 + 8^2 = c^2$

3. $15^2 + b^2 = 17^2$

4. $12^2 + b^2 = 20^2$

5. $a^2 + 21^2 = 29^2$

6. $a^2 + 24^2 = 25^2$

In exercises 7–12, c is the measure of the hypotenuse of a right triangle.
Find the missing measure in each.

7. $a = 8, b = 15, c = ?$

8. $a = 3, c = 5, b = ?$

9. $a = 5, b = 12, c = ?$

10. $a = 1.8, c = 3, b = ?$

11. $a = \sqrt{5}, b = \sqrt{2}, c = ?$

12. $b = 12, c = 15, a = ?$

The measures of three sides of a triangle are given in each of the following.
Determine whether each triangle is a right triangle.

13. 4, 5, 7

14. 11, 12, 16

15. 9, 16, 20

16. $\sqrt{6}, \sqrt{10}, \sqrt{4}$

17. 9, 40, 41

18. 45, 60, 75

19. A 26-foot ladder is leaning against a window sill that is 24 feet above the ground. How far is the foot of the ladder from the building?

20. A rope from the top of a mast on a sailboat is attached to a point 20 feet from the mast. The rope is 29 feet long. How high is the mast?

21. Find the length of the diagonal of a square whose side is 6 ft.

22. Helga decides to take a shortcut to the zoo by walking diagonally across a square field that is 120 yards on each side. To the nearest yard, how many yards shorter is the shortcut than the usual route?

23. William jogged 6 miles due east and then 4.5 miles due north. How far is he from his starting point?

24. A telephone pole is 28 ft high. A wire is stretched from the top of the pole to a point on the ground that is 21 ft from the bottom of the pole. How long is the wire?

Section 6.1

1. yes   **2.** yes   **3.** yes   **4.** no   **5.** no   **6.** yes   **7.** no

8. $m\angle RVZ = 142$, obtuse   **9.** $m\angle TVZ = 90$, right   **10.** $m\angle WVZ = 75$, acute

11. $m\angle YVZ = 25$, acute   **12.** $m\angle QVP = 10$, acute   **13.** $m\angle SVZ = 122$, obtuse

14. $m\angle QVZ = 170$, obtuse   **15.** $m\angle SVP = 58$, acute   **16.** $m\angle YVP = 155$, obtuse

17. $m\angle XVZ = 60$, acute   **18.** $m\angle TVP = 90$, right   **19.** $m\angle WVP = 105$, obtuse

20. $\frac{3}{4}$ of $360° = 270°$ **21.** $\frac{1}{4}$ of $360° = 90°$ **22.** $\frac{1}{8}$ of $360° = 45°$

23. 12.5% of $360° = 45°$ **24.** $\frac{4}{9}$ of $360° = 160°$ **25.** $60°$ is $\frac{1}{6}$ of $360°$

26. $40°$ is $\frac{1}{9}$ of $360°$ **27.** $180°$ is $\frac{1}{2}$ of $360°$ **28.** $x°$ is $\frac{x}{360}$ of $360°$

29. $279°$ is $\frac{279}{360}$ of $360°$

Section 6.2

$m\angle A + m\angle B = 180$

1. $m\angle A + 70 = 180$
$m\angle A = 110$

2. $m\angle A + 45 = 180$
$m\angle A = 135$

3. $m\angle A + 130 = 180$
$m\angle A = 50$

4. $m\angle A + 77 = 180$
$m\angle A = 103$

5. $m\angle A + 110.5 = 180$
$m\angle A = 69.5$

6. $m\angle A + 12\frac{1}{3} = 180$
$m\angle A = 167\frac{2}{0}$

7. $m\angle A + 3.07 = 180$
$m\angle A = 176.93$

8. $m\angle A + x = 180$
$m\angle A = 180 - x$

9. $m\angle M + 65 = 90$
$m\angle M = 25$

10. $m\angle M + 38 = 90$
$m\angle M = 52$

11. $18°31'$ **12.** $73°59'$ **13.** $47°27'50''$ **14.** $23°38'22''$ **15.** $88°18'53''$

16. $(90 - r)°$

17. $x = 32°$
vertical angle

18. $x + 90 + 50 = 180$
$x + 140 = 180$
$x = 40$

19. $x + 20 + 80 = 180$
$x + 100 = 180$
$x = 80$

20. $x = 90 + 46$
$x = 136$

21. $x = 40°$
vertical angle

22. $x + 75 + 90 = 180$
$x + 165 = 180$
$x = 15$

23. $x + 90 = 180$
$x = 90$

24. $x + 80 + 60 = 180$
$x + 140 = 180$
$x = 40$

Section 6.3

1. 2 pairs alternate interior angles
$\angle AGH$, $\angle GHD$, $\angle CHG$, $\angle HGB$

2. 2 pairs consecutive interior angles
$\angle AGH$, $\angle GHC$, $\angle BGH$, $\angle GHD$

3. 4 pairs of corresponding angles
$\angle EGA$, $\angle GHC$, $\angle EGB$, $\angle GHD$, $\angle AGH$, $\angle CHF$,
$\angle HGB$, $\angle FHD$

4. 2 pairs alternate exterior angles
$\angle AGE$, $\angle FHD$, $\angle EGB$, $\angle CHF$

5. $m\angle AGH = 70$
$\angle CHF$ is a corresponding angle to $\angle AGH$ therefore
$m\angle CHF = 70$

6. 4 pairs of vertical angles
$\angle AGE$, $\angle HGB$, $\angle EGB$, $\angle AGH$, $\angle CHG$, $\angle FHD$,
$\angle CHF$, $\angle GHD$

7. $m\angle CHF = 30 + x$
$m\angle EGB = 2x - 15$
$m\angle EGB = m\angle AGH$ vertical angle
$m\angle AGH = m\angle CHF$ corresponding angle
$m\angle CHF = m\angle EGB$
$30 + x = 2x - 15$
$45 = x$

8. $m\angle BGH = \dfrac{x}{2} + 22$
$m\angle DHG = \dfrac{2x - 2}{5}$
$m\angle BGH = m\angle DHF$ corresponding angles
$m\angle DHF + m\angle DHG = 180$ supplementary angles
$\dfrac{x}{2} + 22 + \dfrac{2x - 2}{5} = 180$
$5x + 220 + 4x - 4 = 1800$
$9x + 216 = 1800$
$9x = 1584$
$x = 176$

$m\angle BGH = \dfrac{x}{2} + 22$
$= \dfrac{176}{2} + 22$
$= 88 + 22$
$= 110$

9. $m\angle EGB = 2x + 5$
$m\angle CHG = 3x + 25$
$m\angle EGB = m\angle AGH$ vertical angles
$m\angle AGH = m\angle CHF$ corresponding angles
$m\angle EGB = m\angle CHF$

$m\angle CHF + m\angle CHG = 180$
$2x + 5 + 3x + 25 = 180$
$5x + 30 = 180$
$5x = 150$
$x = 30$
$m\angle EGB = 2 \cdot 30 + 5$
$m\angle EGB = 65$
$m\angle CHF = 65$

10. $m\angle CHG = 100$
$\angle BGH$ is an alternate interior angle to $\angle CHG$
therefore $m\angle CHG = 100$.

Section 6.4

1. scalene, right
2. isosceles, obtuse
3. scalene, right
4. equilateral, acute
5. isosceles, acute
6. scalene, obtuse
7. equilateral, acute
8. scalene, acute
9. 90, 35, 55
10. 15, 15, 150
11. 40, 80, 60
12. 38, 76, 66
13. 90, 40, 50
14. 80, 90, 10
15. 60, 60, 60
16. 30, 35, 115
17. 70, 60, 50
18. 41, 82, 57
19. 62, 63, 55
20. 29, 35, 116

Section 6.5

1. Corresponding sides $\overline{CB}, \overline{DQ}$; $\overline{CA}, \overline{DS}$; $\overline{BA}, \overline{QS}$
Corresponding angles $\angle BCA, \angle QDS$; $\angle CAB, \angle DSQ$; $\angle ABC, \angle SQD$

2. Corresponding sides $\overline{HK}, \overline{LM}$; $\overline{GK}, \overline{PM}$; $\overline{GH}, \overline{PL}$
Corresponding angles $\angle GKH, \angle LMP$; $\angle HGK, \angle LPM$; $\angle GHK, \angle MLP$

3. $\dfrac{a}{d} = \dfrac{b}{e} = \dfrac{c}{f}$
$\dfrac{3}{4} = \dfrac{6}{e} = \dfrac{7}{f}$ $e = 8$
$\dfrac{3}{4} = \dfrac{6}{8} = \dfrac{7}{f}$ $f = 9\dfrac{1}{3}$
$3f = 28$
$f = 9\dfrac{1}{3}$

4. $x = 4,000$; The building is 4000 cm (or 40 m) high.

5. $\angle ABC, \angle DEF$; $\angle BCA, \angle EFD$; $\angle CAB, \angle FDE$

$\overline{AB}, \overline{DE}$; $\overline{BC}, \overline{EF}$; $\overline{AC}, \overline{DF}$

6. $\dfrac{r}{j} = \dfrac{s}{k} = \dfrac{t}{l}$
$\dfrac{3}{5} = \dfrac{15}{k} = \dfrac{14}{l}$ $k = 25$
$\dfrac{3}{5} = \dfrac{15}{25} = \dfrac{14}{l}$ $l = 23\dfrac{1}{3}$
$3l = 70$
$l = 23\dfrac{1}{3}$

7. $x = 20$; The 25' ladder would touch the building 20' above the ground.

8. $x = 240$; The tree is 240 inches (or 20 ft) high.

Section 6.6

1. $8^2 + 15^2 = c^2$
$64 + 225 = c^2$
$289 = c^2$
$17 = c$

2. $6^2 + 8^2 = c^2$
$36 + 64 = c^2$
$100 = c^2$
$10 = c$

3. $15^2 + b^2 = 17^2$
$225 + b^2 = 289$
$b^2 = 64$
$b = 8$

4. $12^2 + b^2 = 20^2$
$144 + b^2 = 400$
$b^2 = 256$
$b = 16$

5. $a^2 + 21^2 = 29^2$
$a^2 + 441 = 841$
$a^2 = 400$
$a = 20$

6. $a^2 + 24^2 = 25^2$
$a^2 + 576 = 625$
$a^2 = 49$
$a = 7$

7. $17 = c$

8. $b = 4$

9. $13 = c$

10. $b = 2.4$

11. $\sqrt{7}$

12. $a = 9$

13. no

14. no

15. no

16. yes

17. yes

18. yes

19. The ladder is 10 ft from the building.

20. The mast is 21 ft high.

21. The diagonal is 8.485 ft long.

22. 70 yards are saved by taking the diagonal.

23. William is 7.5 miles from his starting point.

24. The wire is 35' long.